Answers: P1 — P8

Section One — Number

Page 1 — Types of Number and BODMAS

Q1 **a)** 46, 73, 231, 233, 376, 494, 817, 1101, 1272, 2319
b) 2.34, 2.43, 3.24, 3.42, 4.23, 4.32

Q2 **a)** 40 **b)** 4 **c)** 4000 **d)** 40 000 **e)** 0.04 **f)** 0.4

Q3 **a)** 16 **b)** 49 **c)** 144 **d)** 8 **e)** 27 **f)** 1000

Q4 5, -87, 167

Q5 **a)** 20 **b)** 6 **c)** 33 **d)** 23 **e)** 10 **f)** 52

Q6 $\frac{1}{9}$

Page 2 — Wordy Real-Life Problems

Q1 £6.97

Q2 Package A costs £79.99 × 14 = £1119.86
Package B costs £90 + (£74.99 × 14) = £1139.86.
So package A is cheaper.

Q3 £12

Q4 She needs 4 × 31 × 2 = 248 pens.
248 ÷ 12 = 20.666..., so 21 packs are needed. So the total cost would be 21 × £3.89 = £81.69

Q5 Each pack of T-shirts makes a profit of £20 – (5 × £2.50) = £7.50
£320 ÷ £7.50 ≈ 42.67. So for a £320 profit, Martin needs to sell 43 packs.

Q6 500 flowers produce 1500 stigmas.
1500 × 0.001 = 1.5 g
1.5 × £6 = £9

Page 3 — Multiplying and Dividing by 10, 100, etc.

Q1 **a)** 10 **b)** 1000 **c)** 100 **d)** 1000

Q2 **a)** 80 **b)** 3400 **c)** 436 000 **d)** 2 **e)** 690 **f)** 4730 **g)** 600 **h)** 28 000 **i)** 9 000 000

Q3 £245

Q4 £301

Q5 **a)** 3 **b)** 0.58 **c)** 4 **d)** 0.615 **e)** 0.0296 **f)** 0.7536 **g)** 4 **h)** 12 **i)** 0.213

Q6 1.58 m

Q7 1.4 g

Q8 1.14 euros

Page 4 — Multiplying and Dividing Whole Numbers

Q1 **a)** 212 **b)** 623 **c)** 2470

Q2

Litres	1	6	14	28	47
Cost in pence	121	726	1694	3388	5687

Q3 **a)** 5724 m **b)** 8586 m **c)** 11 448 m

Q4 **a)** 278 **b)** 117 **c)** 26

Q5 Each pays £16

Q6 73 g

Q7 4

Page 5 — Multiplying and Dividing with Decimals

Q1 **a)** 12.8 **b)** 52.6 **c)** 1.767 **d)** 7.92 **e)** 4.912 **f)** 2.884 **g)** 6.213 **h)** 11.664

Q2 **a)** 3.9 **b)** 2.4 **c)** 2.6 **d)** 24.5 **e)** 7 **f)** 20 **g)** 13 **h)** 485

Q3 1.39 m

Q4 **a)** 7.62 cm **b)** 182.88 cm **c)** 4114.8 cm

Page 6 — Negative Numbers

Q1

-5 -4 -3 0 1 2 3 4

Q2 **a)** > **b)** < **c)** >

Q3 2, 0.5, -1.5, -2, -8

Q4 **a)** -2 °C (or a decrease of 2 °C) **b)** -9 °C

Q5 **a)** 4 **b)** -73 **c)** -11 **d)** 6 **e)** -24 **f)** 21

Q6 **a)** [illegible]
c) [illegible] **e)** 24 **f)** 4

Q7 **a)** 49 **b)** 121 **c)** -27

Q8 **a)** -6 **b)** -2 **c)** 1 **d)** 2

Page 7 — Prime Numbers

Q1 2, 3, 5, 7, 11, 13, 17, 19, 23, 29

Q2 E.g. 27 is divisible by 3

Q3 **a)** 2 **b)** E.g. 23 or 37 **c)** 11, 13 or 17 **d)** 13 and 7 or 17 and 3 **e)** E.g. 1 or 21

Q4 41, 43, 47

Q5 (circled numbers shown in bold)

1	**2**	**3**	4	**5**	6	**7**	8	9	10
11	12	**13**	14	15	16	**17**	18	**19**	20
21	22	**23**	24	25	26	27	28	**29**	30
31	32	33	34	35	36	**37**	38	39	40
41	42	**43**	44	45	46	**47**	48	49	50
51	52	**53**	54	55	56	57	58	**59**	60
61	62	63	64	65	66	**67**	68	69	70
71	72	**73**	74	75	76	77	78	**79**	80
81	82	**83**	84	85	86	87	88	**89**	90
91	92	93	94	95	96	**97**	98	99	100

Q6 Judo and kendo as 29 and 23 are prime.

Q7 E.g. 2 + 3 + 5 = 10,
5 + 11 + 13 = 29,
11 + 13 + 17 = 41

Pages 8-9 — Multiples, Factors and Prime Factors

Q1 **a)** 4, 8, 12, 16, 20 **b)** 7, 14, 21, 28, 35 **c)** 12, 24, 36, 48, 60 **d)** 18, 36, 54, 72, 90

Q2 **a)** 12 **b)** 35 **c)** 42 **d)** 180
Other answers are possible here — ask your teacher.

Q3 24
Other answers are possible.

Q4 **a)** 24 **b)** 48 **c)** 72
Other answers are possible.

Answers: P8 — P15

Q5 **a)** 14, 20, 22, 50, 70
b) 20, 35, 50, 55, 70
c) 14, 35, 70, 77
d) 22, 55, 77, 99

Q6 1, 2, 3, 4, 5, 6, 8, 9, 10 should all be circled.

Q7 Any 4 of:
2 groups of 18, 3 groups of 12,
4 groups of 9, 6 groups of 6,
9 groups of 4, 12 groups of 3,
18 groups of 2.

Q8 **a)** 6
b) 36

Q9

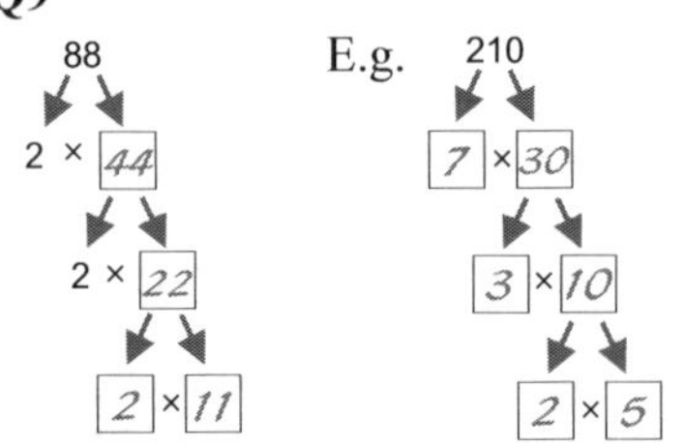

88 = 2×2×2×11 210 = 2×3×5×7

Q10 **a)** 2×3^3
b) $2^2 \times 5 \times 7$
c) 3^4
d) $2 \times 5^2 \times 11$

Pages 10-11 — LCM and HCF

Q1 **a)** 6, 12, 18, 24, 30, 36, 42, 48, 54, 60
b) 5, 10, 15, 20, 25, 30, 35, 40, 45, 50
c) 30

Q2 **a)** 15 **b)** 24
c) 30 **d)** 90
e) 42 **f)** 132

Q3 **a)** 1 **b)** 2
c) 5 **d)** 3
e) 7 **f)** 11

Q4 **a)** 7th June (i.e. 6 days later, since 6 is the LCM of 2 and 3)
b) 16th June (i.e. 15 days later, since 15 is the LCM of 3 and 5)
c) Sunday (30 days later, since 30 is the LCM of 2, 3 and 5 — i.e. 4 weeks and 2 days later)
d) Lars (it's 14 days after 1st June, and 14 is a multiple of 2 but not 3 or 5)

Q5 **a)** $36 = 2 \times 2 \times 3 \times 3$
$24 = 2 \times 2 \times 2 \times 3$
b) $2 \times 2 \times 2 \times 3 \times 3 = 72$
c) $2 \times 2 \times 3 = 12$

Q6 **a)** $2 \times 2 \times 2 \times 2 \times 3 \times 5 = 240$
b) $2 \times 3 \times 5 = 30$
c) $2 \times 2 \times 2 \times 2 \times 3 \times 3 = 144$
d) $2 \times 7 = 14$

Q7 Evan would have to make at least 72 sandwiches to have nothing left in any of the packets (because 72 is the LCM of 9, 6 and 8). This corresponds to 8 packs of bread rolls, 12 packs of cheese and 9 packs of ham.

Q8 **a)** 18 (because 18 is the HCF of 36, 54 and 72)
b) $(36 \div 18) + (54 \div 18) + (72 \div 18) = 9$

Pages 12-13 — Fractions Without a Calculator

Q1 E.g.

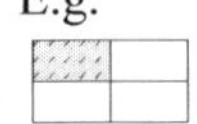
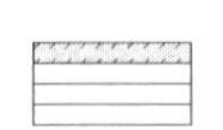

E.g.

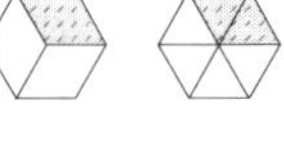

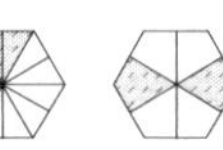

Q2 **a)** $\frac{1}{4}$ **b)** $\frac{3}{4}$ **c)** $\frac{1}{3}$
d) $\frac{2}{3}$ **e)** $\frac{1}{3}$ **f)** $\frac{3}{4}$

Q3 **a)** $1\frac{1}{2}$ **b)** $1\frac{3}{4}$ **c)** $2\frac{2}{3}$

Q4 **a)** $\frac{5}{2}$ **b)** $\frac{10}{3}$ **c)** $\frac{8}{5}$

Q5 **a)** 1 **b)** $\frac{2}{3}$ **c)** $\frac{1}{6}$
d) $\frac{3}{10}$ **e)** $\frac{22}{15}$ **f)** $\frac{25}{48}$

Q6 **a)** $1\frac{1}{2}$ **b)** $3\frac{3}{5}$ **c)** 12
d) $2\frac{2}{3}$ **e)** 8 **f)** $7\frac{2}{9}$

Q7 **a)** $\frac{1}{2} = \frac{2}{4} = \frac{3}{6} = \frac{4}{8} = \frac{5}{10} = \frac{25}{50} = \frac{35}{70} = \frac{50}{100}$
b) $\frac{200}{300} = \frac{100}{150} = \frac{10}{15} = \frac{40}{60} = \frac{120}{180} = \frac{6}{9} = \frac{2}{3}$
c) $\frac{7}{10} = \frac{14}{20} = \frac{21}{30} = \frac{210}{300} = \frac{49}{70} = \frac{28}{40}$

Q8 **a)** $\frac{1}{5}, \frac{3}{10}$
b) $\frac{6}{21}, \frac{3}{7}$
c) $\frac{4}{6}, \frac{11}{15}, \frac{4}{5}$
d) $\frac{1}{3}, \frac{5}{12}, \frac{4}{6}$

Q9 **a)** $\frac{5}{4}$ **b)** $\frac{5}{6}$ **c)** $\frac{13}{12}$
d) $\frac{25}{12}$ **e)** $\frac{48}{5}$ **f)** $\frac{63}{8}$

Q10 **a)** $4\frac{1}{15}$ **b)** $3\frac{8}{9}$ **c)** $1\frac{7}{10}$
d) $2\frac{5}{6}$ **e)** $4\frac{1}{2}$ **f)** $1\frac{11}{20}$

Q11 **a)** $32 \div 8 = 4$
b) $144 \div 12 = 12$
c) $(25 \div 5) \times 4 = 20$
d) $(63 \div 9) \times 7 = 49$
e) $(100 \div 10) \times 3 = 30$
f) $(264 \div 11) \times 3 = 72$

Page 14 — Fraction Problems

Q1 £45

Q2 **a)** $\frac{1}{12}$ **b)** $\frac{1}{4}$ **c)** $\frac{2}{3}$

Q3 **a)** $\frac{3}{4}$ of the programme
b) $\frac{5}{8}$ of the programme
c) $\frac{1}{8}$ of the programme

Q4 **a)** $\frac{9}{15} = \frac{3}{5}$ **b)** $\frac{18}{45} = \frac{2}{5}$

Q5 **a)** $\frac{2}{15}$
b) $\frac{2}{3} - \frac{2}{15} = \frac{8}{15}$

Q6 £15

Q7 4.8 g = $\frac{3}{4}$ of the original amount
original amount = 4.8 ÷ 3 × 4 = 6.4 g

Q8 Charity: £400, Tax: £400,
Left over: £1600.

Pages 15-16 — Fractions, Decimals and Percentages

Q1 **a)** 0.5 **b)** 0.75
c) 0.7 **d)** 0.95
e) 0.01 **f)** 0.375
g) 0.002 **h)** 0.02

Q2 **a)** 25% **b)** 30%
c) 80% **d)** 148%
e) 108% **f)** 5%
g) 137.5% **h)** $36\frac{2}{3}$%

Q3 **a)** 62% **b)** 74%
c) 40% **d)** 90%
e) 7% **f)** 2%
g) 12.5% **h)** 98.7%

Q4 **a)** 0.25 **b)** 0.49
c) 0.03 **d)** 0.3

Q5 **a)** $\frac{3}{4}$ **b)** $\frac{3}{5}$
c) $\frac{3}{20}$ **d)** $\frac{53}{100}$

Q6 **a)** $\frac{1}{2}$ **b)** $\frac{4}{5}$
c) $\frac{19}{100}$ **d)** $\frac{1}{4}$

Answers: P15 — P23

e) $\frac{16}{25}$ **f)** $\frac{3}{50}$
g) $\frac{1}{8}$ **h)** $\frac{3}{40}$

Q7 0.343, $\frac{3}{8}$, 55%, 0.61, 68%, $\frac{16}{20}$

Q8 **a)** $0.\dot{2}$ **d)** $0.6\dot{7}$
b) $0.\dot{3}4\dot{6}$ **e)** $0.\dot{3}85\dot{4}$
c) $0.\dot{1}\dot{9}$ **f)** $0.48\dot{3}$

Q9 **a)** $4 \div 9 = 0.444... = 0.\dot{4}$
b) $3 \div 11 = 0.2727... = 0.\dot{2}\dot{7}$
c) $2 \div 3 = 0.666... = 0.\dot{6}$
d) $5 \div 6 = 0.8333... = 0.8\dot{3}$
e) $7 \div 11 = 0.6363... = 0.\dot{6}\dot{3}$
f) $5 \div 12 = 0.41666... = 0.41\dot{6}$

Q10 **a)** > **b)** < **c)** <

Q11 Khaled: 125 out of 200 = 62.5%
Sebastian: 64%, Sienna: $\frac{18}{25}$ = 72%
So Sienna has read the most.

Q12 Loaf A: $\frac{17}{20}$ = 85%, Loaf B: 82%
Loaf C: 9 : 1 means $\frac{9}{9+1} = \frac{9}{10}$
= 90% of the flour is white.
So loaf C has the greatest proportion of white flour.

Pages 17-18 — Rounding Numbers

Q1 **a)** 3 **b)** 27
c) 2 **d)** 11
e) 6 **f)** 44
g) 10 **h)** 0

Q2 2

Q3 **a)** £4 **b)** £17
c) £12 **d)** £8
e) £1 **f)** £15
g) £7 **h)** £0
i) £10

Q4 **a)** 20 **b)** 80
c) 70 **d)** 100
e) 120 **f)** 240
g) 960 **h)** 1060

Q5 **a)** 600 **b)** 800
c) 200 **d)** 500
e) 1300 **f)** 3300
g) 3000

Q6 **a)** 23 000
b) 37 000
c) 50 000

Q7 **a)** 17.36 **b)** 38.06
c) 0.74 **d)** 6.00
e) 4.30 **f)** 7.04

Q8 **a)** 6.353 **b)** 81.645
c) 0.008 **d)** 53.270
e) 754.400 **f)** 0.000

Q9 £8.57

Q10 **a)** 10 **b)** 500
c) 1000 **d)** 0.02
e) 2000 **f)** 0.3

Q11 **a)** 1380 **b)** 1330
c) 0.296 **d)** 0.0214

Q12 5.1

Q13 1.70

Q14 **a)** 2 **b)** 1
c) 12 **d)** 0
e) 2 **f)** 2

Page 19 — Estimating

Q1 **a)** $20 \times 10 = 200$
b) $60 \times 50 = 3000$
c) $100 \times 100 = 10\ 000$
d) $20 \div 5 = 4$
e) $900 \div 30 = 30$
f) $1000 \div 500 = 2$
(Other answers are possible depending on the approximations used.)

Q2 **a)** 24 000 ÷ 12 = £2000
b) 1000 + (0.1 × 24 000) = £3400
c) 24 000 – (24 000 × 0.1) = £21 600
(Other answers are possible.)

Q3 **a)** $\frac{60 \times 10}{5} = 120$
b) $\frac{30 \times 6}{2} = 90$
c) $\frac{3 \times 50}{0.5} = 150 \times 2 = 300$
d) $\frac{5 \times 8}{0.1} = 40 \times 10 = 400$
(Other answers are possible.)

Q4 **a)** $\frac{\sqrt{4 \times 9}}{9 - 6} = \frac{6}{3} = 2$
b) $\sqrt{\frac{80 + 1}{3 \times 3}} = \frac{9}{3} = 3$

Q5 Estimate is likely to be lower than actual value, as all numbers have been rounded down.

Page 20 — Rounding Errors

Q1 Accept 3.5 - 4.5 m

Q2 75

Q3 **a)** 195 cm $\leq l <$ 205 cm
b) 105 cm

Q4 545 cm

Q5 **a)** 300.6 m $\leq h <$ 300.7 m
b) 125.25 m

Page 21 — Powers

Q1 **a)** $2^4 = 2 \times 2 \times 2 \times 2 = 16$
b) $3^5 = 3 \times 3 \times 3 \times 3 \times 3 = 243$
c) $10^6 = 10 \times 10 \times 10 \times 10 \times 10 \times 10 = 1\ 000\ 000$

Q2 **a)** 2^8 **b)** 12^5
c) m^3 **d)** y^4

Q3 **a)** 248 832
b) 2197
c) 551.368
d) 0.03125

Q4 **c)** $6^3 \times 6^5 = 6^{3+5} = 6^8$
d) $12^8 \div 12^2 = 12^{8-2} = 12^6$
e) $7^{22} \div 7^{15} = 7^{22-15} = 7^7$
f) $13^6 \times 13 = 13^{6+1} = 13^7$
g) $3^{14} \div 3^9 = 3^{14-9} = 3^5$
h) $8^{12} \times 8^3 = 8^{12+3} = 8^{15}$

Q5 **b)** $(3^8)^4 = 3^{8 \times 4} = 3^{32}$
c) $(21^2)^6 = 21^{2 \times 6} = 21^{12}$
d) $(17^5)^8 = 17^{5 \times 8} = 17^{40}$

Q6 **a)** $\frac{5^8 \times 5^3}{5^3 \times 5^6} = \frac{5^{11}}{5^9} = 5^2 = 25$
b) $\frac{7^0}{7^1 \times 7^1} = \frac{1}{7^2} = \frac{1}{49}$

Q7 **a)** $2^{-5} = \frac{1}{2^5} = \frac{1}{32}$
b) $8^{-2} = \frac{1}{8^2} = \frac{1}{64}$
c) $\left(\frac{3}{2}\right)^{-2} = \left(\frac{2}{3}\right)^2 = \frac{2^2}{3^2} = \frac{4}{9}$
d) $\left(\frac{3}{5}\right)^{-3} = \left(\frac{5}{3}\right)^3 = \frac{5^3}{3^3} = \frac{125}{27}$

Page 22 — Roots

Q1 **a)** 8 **g)** 27
b) 4 **h)** 1
c) 6 **i)** 13
d) 14 **j)** 85
e) 23 **k)** 1000
f) 9 **l)** 5

Q2 **a)** 2 and -2
b) 4 and -4
c) 3 and -3
d) 7 and -7
e) 5 and -5
f) 10 and -10
g) 12 and -12
h) 8 and -8
i) 9 and -9

Q3 **a)** 16 **d)** 100
b) 12 **e)** 1
c) 11 **f)** 0.5

Q4 **a)** 4 **c)** 10
b) 3 **d)** 2

Q5 **a)** 9 **c)** 6
b) 3 **d)** 2

Q6 5 cm

Q7 240 m

Q8 **a)** 52.51 **b)** 49.32

Page 23 — Standard Form

Q1 **a)** 3.67×10^4
b) 5.4×10^{-2}

Answers: P23 — P29

c) 1.94×10^5
d) 2.8×10^2
e) 8.11×10^{-4}
f) 7.92×10^{-5}

Q2 a) 38 600
b) 0.000051
c) 2 620 000
d) 0.00137
e) 6050
f) 0.0004621

Q3 a) Mercury
b) Jupiter
c) Mercury
d) Neptune

Q4 a) 6×10^6 c) 8.6×10^5
b) 2×10^2 d) 3.4×10^7

Q5 a) 8×10^2 c) 1.2×10^{-4}
b) 2.45×10^{-5} d) 1.76×10^7

Section Two — Algebra

Page 24 — Simplifying

Q1 b) 0
c) $25f - 15$
d) $28x - 1$
e) $15x - y$
f) $35a + 24b$
g) $-6f - 14g$
h) $12a^2 + 16a - 3$

Q2 b) $5x^2 + 3x - 1$
c) $3x^2 - 4x + 18$
d) $6y^2 + 9y - 5$
e) $a^2 - 4a + 4$
f) $-3x^2 - 5x + 7$
g) $3x^2 + 9x$
h) $5y^2 - 2y - 6$

Q3 a) b^5
b) $4cd$
c) $12ef$
d) $15g^3$
e) $56h^2$
f) $2j^3k$
g) $\frac{2}{3}p$
h) $2n$

Q4 a) $7 + 3\sqrt{3}$
b) $3 + 2\sqrt{2}$
c) $4 + 5\sqrt{5}$
d) $3 - \sqrt{6}$

Page 25 — Multiplying Out Brackets

Q1 b) $4x - 12$
c) $8x^2 + 16$
d) $-2x - 2y$
e) $-3y - 12$
f) $10 - 5y$
g) $x^2 + 8x$
h) $3x^2 + 3xy$

Q2 a) $10a + 12b$
b) $9x + 7y$
c) $-3a - 4b$
d) $4e^2 - ef$
e) $6x^2 + 2x$
f) $11 - 2ab$
g) $2x - 4y - 2x^2 - 2xz$
h) $x^3 + x^2$

Q3 a) $x^2 + 3x + 2$
b) $x^2 + 2x - 15$
c) $x^2 + 13x + 30$
d) $x^2 - 7x + 10$
e) $x^2 - 11x + 28$
f) $2x^2 + 7x + 3$
g) $6x^2 - 12x + 4x - 8 = 6x^2 - 8x - 8$
h) $6x - 2 + 9x^2 - 3x = 9x^2 + 3x - 2$

Q4 a) $x^2 - 2x + 1$
b) $x^2 + 6x + 9$
c) $4x^2 - 20x + 25$
d) $16x^2 + 24x + 9$

Page 26 — Factorising

Q1 a) $4(x + 2)$
b) $4(3 - 2x)$
c) $4(1 - 4x)$
d) $4(6x + 7)$
e) $4(8 - 5x)$
f) $4(x^2 + 16)$

Q2 a) $x(2 + x)$
b) $x(2 - x)$
c) $x(x - 7)$
d) $x(1 - 16x)$
e) $x(4x - 3)$
f) $x(6 + 13x)$

Q3 a) $2(x + 2)$
b) $3(x + 4)$
c) $12(2 + x)$
d) $4(4x + y)$
e) $3(x + 5)$
f) $10(3 + x)$
g) $3x(3x + 1)$
h) $5x(x + 2)$
i) $7x(x + 3)$
j) $4x(2x + 1)$

Q4 a) $y(3 + xy)$
b) $a(1 + 2ab)$
c) $2m(2n^2 + 1)$
d) $3g(gh - 3)$

Q5 a) $(x + 3)(x - 3)$
b) $(y + 4)(y - 4)$
c) $(5 + z)(5 - z)$
d) $(6 + a)(6 - a)$

Q6 a) $(2x + 3)(2x - 3)$
b) $(3y + 2)(3y - 2)$
c) $(5 + 4z)(5 - 4z)$
d) $(1 + 6a)(1 - 6a)$

Page 27 — Solving Equations

Q1 a) $a = 14$ b) $b = 18$
c) $h = 25$ d) $f = -10$
e) $i = 84$ f) $k = 9.3$

Q2 a) $m = 7$ b) $p = 43$
c) $r = -1.5$ d) $t = 55$
e) $w = 108$ f) $v = 112$

Q3 a) $x = 4$ b) $x = 7$
c) $x = 7$ d) $x = 18$
e) $x = 18$ f) $x = 200$

Q4 a) $x = 5$ b) $x = 3$
c) $x = 6$ d) $x = 2$
e) $x = 4$ f) $x = 1$

Q5 a) $x = 2$ b) $x = 10$
c) $x = 9$

Q6 a) $x = 5$ or $x = -5$
b) $y = 4$ or $y = -4$
c) $u = 3$ or $u = -3$

Page 28 — Expressions, Formulas and Functions

Q1 23

Q2 40

Q3 a) 520p or £5.20
b) 450p or £4.50

Q4 a) 47 sheep in each field.
b) 82 sheep in each field.

Q5 30 minutes

Q6 28.5

Q7 10.44

Q8 a) $y = 14$
b) $x = 11$

Page 29 — Formulas and Equations from Words

Q1 a) $n + 3$
b) $n - 4$
c) $n \times 2$ or $2n$

Q2 $4x + 3$

Q3 $y + 4y = 20$
$5y = 20$
$y = 4$, so she has 4 cats.

Q4 a) $C = 5h + 10$
b) 7.5 hours (7 hours 30 minutes)

Q5 a) $c = 1.5 + 1.4m$
b) $m = (c - 1.5) / 1.4 = 6$ miles

Q6 $x + 3x + 3x - 5 = 23$
$7x - 5 = 23$
$x = 4$
Therefore, Frances has 4, Millicent has 12 and Winston has 7.

Q7 $5(18.5 + x) + 5 = 116$
$x = £3.70$

Answers: P30 — P35

Page 30 — Formulas and Equations from Diagrams

Q1 **a)** $3x + x + 3x + x = 8x$ cm
b) $8x = 36$
$x = 4.5$

Q2 $5(x - 1) = 2x + 1$
$5x - 5 = 2x + 1$
$3x = 6$, so $x = 2$
Side length is $(2 \times 2) + 1 = 5$ cm

Q3 **a)** $P = 2y + 4y - 1 + 4y - 1$
$P = 10y - 2$
b) $10y - 2 = 13$
$10y = 15$
$y = 1.5$

Q4 The parallelogram's area is
$2(5n - 4) \times 2 = 20n - 16$
The square's area is $8^2 = 64$ cm^2.
So $20n - 16 = 64$
$20n = 80$
$n = 4$

Q5 Rectangle's perimeter $= 32b - 22$
Square's perimeter $= 16b$
So $32b - 22 = 16b + 2$
$16b = 24$
$b = 1.5$
So one side of the square is
$4 \times 1.5 = 6$ cm

Q6 Area of right-angled triangle
$= 0.5 \times 5(x + 1) \times 4 = 10x + 10$
Area of other triangle
$= 0.5 \times 10(4x - 5)$
$= 20x - 25$
$10x + 10 = 20x - 25$
$35 = 10x$, so $x = 3.5$

Page 31 — Rearranging Formulas

Q1 **a)** $x = y - 4$
b) $x = (y - 3)/2$
c) $x = (y + 5)/4$
d) $b = (a - 10)/7$
e) $z = (w - 14)/2$
f) $t = (s + 3)/4$
g) $x = (y - ½)/3$
h) $x = 3 - y$
i) $x = y/5 - 2$

Q2 **a)** $x = 10y$ **e)** $g = 8f/3$
b) $t = 14s$ **f)** $x = 5y - 5$
c) $b = 3a/2$ **g)** $x = 2y + 6$
d) $e = 4d/3$ **h)** $b = 3a + 15$

Q3 **a)** $x = \pm\sqrt{y}$
b) $x = \pm\sqrt{\frac{y}{2}}$
c) $x = \pm\sqrt{y + 3}$
d) $x = \pm\sqrt{y - 4}$
e) $x = \pm\sqrt{\frac{y}{5}}$
f) $x = \pm\sqrt{y + 11}$

Q4 **a)** $x = \frac{1}{y}$ **c)** $x = \frac{1}{y + 5}$
b) $x = \frac{3}{y}$ **d)** $x = \frac{1}{y - 6}$

Q5 **a)** $y = \frac{x}{z + 1}$ **d)** $y = \frac{m}{2p + 1}$
b) $y = \frac{z}{1 - n}$ **e)** $y = \frac{3}{x - 1}$
c) $y = \frac{a}{2 - c}$ **f)** $y = \frac{5}{3a - 2}$

Pages 32-33 — Sequences

Q1 **a)**
4, 7, 10, 13, 16
b)
12, 19, 26, 33, 40

Q2 **a)** 9, 11, 13, add 2 each time
b) 1, 0.5, 0.25, divide by 2 each time
c) 30 000, 300 000, 3 000 000, multiply by 10 each time
d) -1, -5, -9, subtract 4 each time
e) 25.6, 102.4, 409.6, multiply by 4 each time.

Q3 **a)** 16, 22, 29
b) 37, 50, 65
c) 36, 48, 62

Q4 **a)**
b) The rule is 'square the number of the pattern', so the 6th pattern will have $6^2 = 36$ rectangles.

Q5 **a)** $(3 \times 2) + 1 = 7$
$(3 \times 3) + 1 = 10$
$(3 \times 4) + 1 = 13$
b) 3, 8, 13, 18, 23
c) 1, 4, 9, 16, 25

Q6 **a)** Each term is the sum of the two previous terms.
b) 39, 63, 102

Q7 No. The sequence starts with an odd number and adds an even number on each time, so all terms in the sequence must be odd.

Q8 **a)** 37
b) Setting 3n + 7 = 53 and solving does not give a whole number value of n. So 53 is not a term in the sequence.

Q9 **a)** $2n$ **b)** $2n - 1$
c) $3n + 1$

Q10 **a)** £65 **b)** £95
c) $15n + 20$ **d)** £290

Page 34 — Inequalities

Q1 **a)** $0 \le x \le 4$
b) $-1 \le x < 3$
c) $9 < x \le 13$
d) $-3 < x < 1$
e) $-4 \le x$
f) $x < 5$
g) $0 < x < 2$
h) $-15 \le x \le -14$
i) $25 < x$
j) $-1 < x \le 3$
k) $0 < x < 5$
l) $x < 0$

Q2 **a)**
4 5 6 7 8 9 10

b)
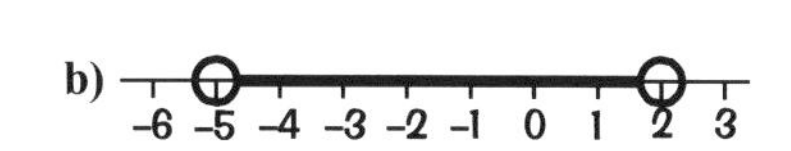

c)
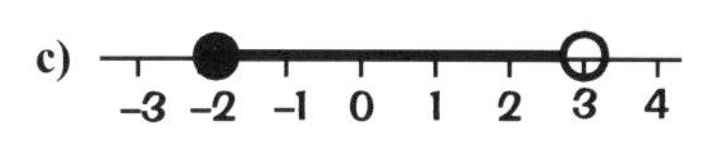

d)
–4 –3 –2 –1 0 1 2

Q3 -2, -1, 0, 1, 2, 3

Q4 **a)** $x \ge 8$ **g)** $x > 40$
b) $x > -5$ **h)** $x \le 3$
c) $x > 3$ **i)** $x < 4$
d) $x \le 13$ **j)** $x \le 5$
e) $x > -1/5$ **k)** $x \le 6$
f) $x \ge 7$ **l)** $x \ge 7\frac{1}{2}$

Q5 **a)** $x \ge 3$ **c)** $x \le 1$
b) $x < 5$ **d)** $x > 9$

Q6 $x = 6$

Page 35 — Quadratic Equations

Q1 **a)** $(x + 1)(x + 2)$
b) $(x + 1)(x - 8)$
c) $(x - 3)(x - 5)$
d) $(x - 6)(x + 3)$
e) $(x - 1)(x - 4)$
f) $(x + 2)(x + 3)$

Q2 **a)** $(x + 5)(x - 2) = 0$
$x = -5, x = 2$
b) $(x - 3)(x - 2) = 0$
$x = 3, x = 2$
c) $(x - 1)^2 = 0$
$x = 1$
d) $(x - 3)(x - 1) = 0$
$x = 3, x = 1$
e) $(x - 5)(x + 4) = 0$
$x = 5, x = -4$
f) $(x + 7)^2 = 0$
$x = -7$

Answers: P35 — P40

Q3 **a)** $(x + 8)(x - 2) = 0$
$x = -8, x = 2$
b) $(x + 9)(x - 4) = 0$
$x = -9, x = 4$
c) $(x + 9)(x - 5) = 0$
$x = -9, x = 5$
d) $x(x - 5) = 0$
$x = 0, x = 5$
e) $x(x - 11) = 0$
$x = 0, x = 11$
f) $(x - 7)(x + 3) = 0$
$x = 7, x = -3$
g) $(x - 24)(x - 2) = 0$
$x = 24, x = 2$
h) $(x - 9)(x - 4) = 0$
$x = 9, x = 4$

Q4 **a)** $(x^2 - x)$ m^2 or $x(x - 1)$ m^2
b) $x^2 - x = 6$, so $x^2 - x - 6 = 0$
$(x - 3)(x + 2) = 0$
$x = 3, x = -2$
You can't have a negative length, so $x = 3$.

Q5 $x(x + 3) = 28$
$x^2 + 3x - 28 = 0$
$(x + 7)(x - 4) = 0$
$x = 4$ (x must be positive)

Page 36 — Simultaneous Equations

Q1 **a)** $x = 1, y = 2$
b) $x = 0, y = 3$
c) $x = -1, y = 4$
d) $x = -2, y = 4$
e) $x = 3, y = 1$
f) $x = 2, y = 5$
g) $x = 3, y = -4$
h) $x = 10, y = 6$

Q2 **a)** $x = 2, y = 3$
b) $x = 4, y = 5$
c) $x = 6, y = -4$
d) $x = 5, y = 2$

Q3 **a)** $x = 1, y = 2$
b) $x = 2, y = 3$
c) $x = 3, y = 1$
d) $x = 2, y = 1$
e) $x = 3, y = 5$
f) $x = 0.5, y = 2$

Q4 Drink: £1.50, ice cream: £2

Page 37 — Proof

Q1 **a)** $(n + 5)^2 - (n + 1)^2$
$\equiv n^2 + 10n + 25 - n^2 - 2n - 1$
$\equiv 8n + 24 \equiv 8(n + 3)$
b) $(n - 3)^2 - (n + 1)(n - 1)$
$\equiv n^2 - 6n + 9 - n^2 + 1$
$\equiv 10 - 6n \equiv 2(5 - 3n)$
c) $n(n - 1) + (n - 2)(3 - n)$
$\equiv n^2 - n + 5n - 6 - n^2$
$\equiv 4n - 6 \equiv 2(2n - 3)$

Q2 2 is a prime number as it only divides by 1 and itself. 2 is even so Maisy is wrong.

Q3 E.g. 3 and 1 are both odd numbers but if you add them together you get 4, which is even so Timothy is wrong.

Q4 **a)** E.g. $1 = 1^2$ and $9 = 3^2$
$9 - 1 = 8$ which is even.
b) $13 \times 6 = 3 \times 26 = 78$
c) E.g. $4 \times 5 = 20$
$20^2 = 400$ which does not end in 4 or 6.

Q5 $x = 3(y + 3) + 2(y - 2)$
$= 3y + 9 + 2y - 4$
$= 5y + 5$
$= 5(y + 1)$ which is a multiple of 5.

Q6 $15n + 24 = 3(m + 2n)$
$15n + 24 = 3m + 6n$
$3m = 9n + 24$
$m = 3n + 8 = 3(n + 2) + 2$
$3(n + 2)$ is a multiple of 3 so $3(n + 2) + 2$ is not a multiple of 3.

Section Three — Graphs

Page 38 — Coordinates and Midpoints

Q1 **a)** (2, 2) **b)** (-1, 2)
c) (0, -1) **d)** (-1, -2.5)

Q2 **a)** (3 , 4) **d)** (8 , 9)
b) (5 , 5) **e)** (2 , 2)
c) (6 , 11) **f)** (6 , -3)

Q3 (-2, 7)

Q4 **a)** (5, 6) **b)** (4, 0)
c) (-15, 18)

Q5 (110, 135)

Page 39 — Drawing Straight-Line Graphs

Q1, Q2 b), Q3 b)

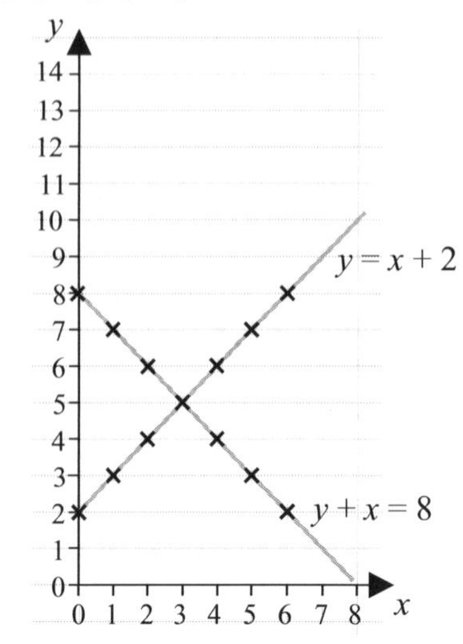

Q2 **a)**

x	0	1	2	3	4	5	6
y	2	3	4	5	6	7	8

Q3 **a)**

x	0	1	2	3	4	5	6
y	8	7	6	5	4	3	2

Q4 **a)**

x	0	5	10	15	20	25	30
y	30	40	50	60	70	80	90

b)

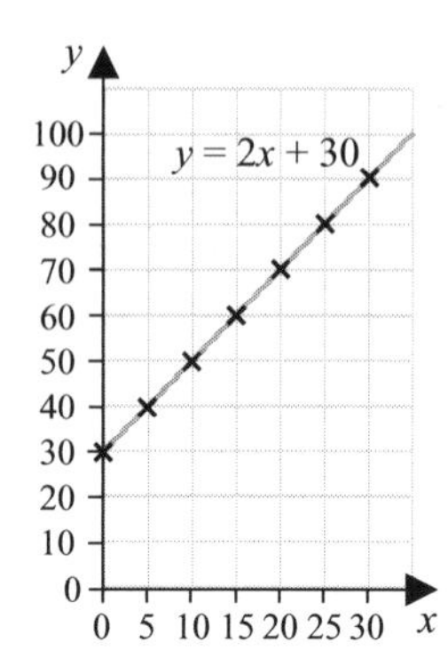

Q5 **a), c)**

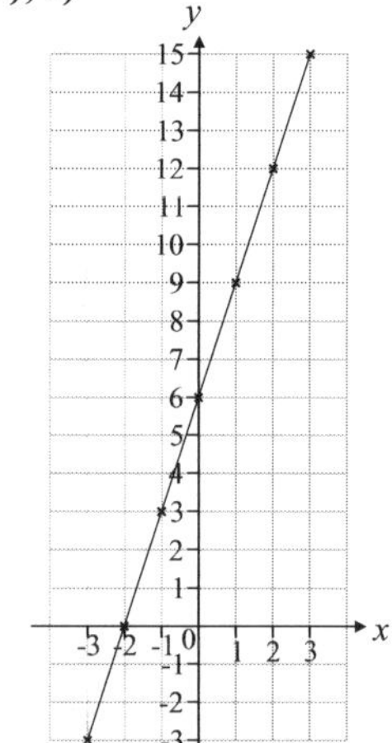

b)

x	-3	-2	-1	0	1	2	3
y	-3	0	3	6	9	12	15

Page 40 — Straight-Line Graphs — Gradients

Q1 **a)** $-\frac{1}{2}$ **f)** $-\frac{8}{3}$
b) 3 **g)** 4
c) $-\frac{1}{4}$ **h)** 1
d) -2 **i)** -1
e) $-\frac{2}{3}$ **j)** $\frac{1}{3}$

Q2 **a)** 2 **c)** -2
b) -1 **d)** $-\frac{3}{4}$

Q3 **a)** B **f)** F
b) A **g)** C
c) F **h)** B
d) G **i)** D
e) E **j)** H

Q4 a), b) and d) are straight lines.

Answers: P41 — P44

Page 41 — Straight-Line Graphs — y = mx + c

Q1 **a)** gradient = 4, intercept = 2
b) gradient = 5, intercept = -1
c) gradient = 6, intercept = 0
d) gradient = 2, intercept = 5
e) gradient = 1, intercept = 0
f) gradient = -1, intercept = 3
g) gradient = -2, intercept = 10
h) gradient = 1/2, intercept = 2

Q2 $m = 3$, $c = 8$

Q3 A; $m = 1$, $c = 3$, $y = x + 3$
B; $m = 2$, $c = 5$, $y = 2x + 5$
C; $m = 1/2$, $c = -4$, $y = \frac{1}{2}x - 4$
D; $m = -1$, $c = 7$, $y = -x + 7$

Q4 **a)** (7, 20), (5, 14)
b) (-1, 0)
c) (-4, 37), (2, -5)

Page 42 — Using y = mx + c

Q1 Pairs a), b), g) circled.

Q2 **a)** $m = 3$
b) $y = 3x + 1$

Q3 **a)** $y = x + 4$
b) $y = 3x + 2$
c) $y = -x$
d) $y = -3x + 4$

Q4 **a)** $y = 2x + 3$
b) $y = x - 8$
c) $y = -5x + 16$
d) $y = 8x - 12$

Q5 **a)** $y = x$ **c)** $y = -3x + 3$
b) $y = 3x$ **d)** $y = -2x - 4$

Q6 **a)** $a = 7$ **b)** $b = 9$ **c)** $c = 4$

Page 43 — Quadratic Graphs

Q1

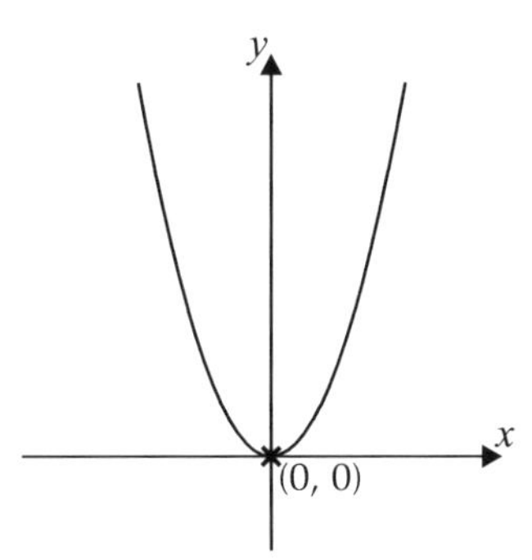

Q2 a)

x	-4	-3	-2	-1	0	1	2	3	4
x^2	16	9	4	1	0	1	4	9	16
$y=2x^2$	32	18	8	2	0	2	8	18	32

b)

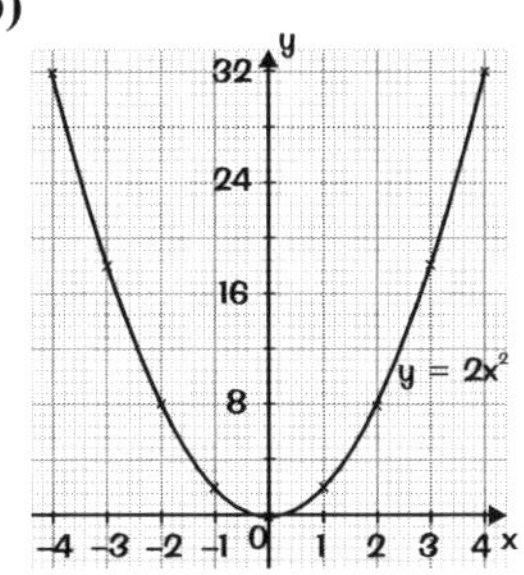

Q3 a)

x	-2	-1	0	1	2	3	4
x^2	4	1	0	1	4	9	16
$-4x$	8	4	0	-4	-8	-12	-16
1	1	1	1	1	1	1	1
$y=x^2-4x+1$	13	6	1	-2	-3	-2	1

b) & c)

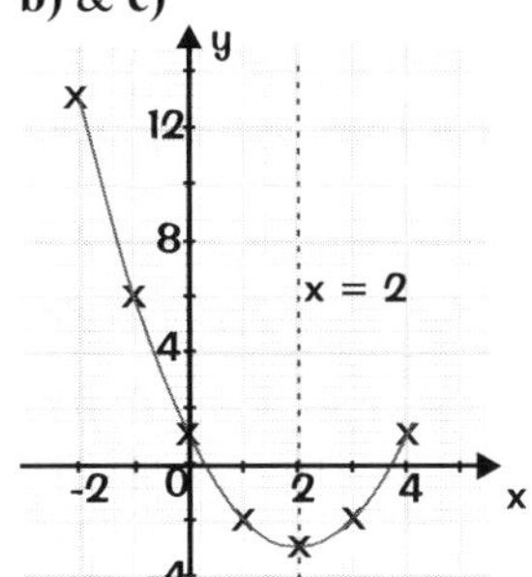

Q4 a)

x	-4	-3	-2	-1	0	1	2	3	4
3	3	3	3	3	3	3	3	3	3
$-x^2$	-16	-9	-4	-1	0	-1	-4	-9	-16
$y=3-x^2$	-13	-6	-1	2	3	2	-1	-6	-13

b)

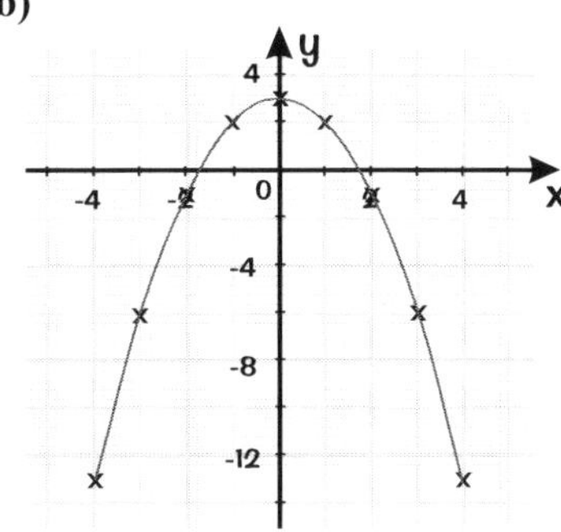

Q5 **a)** c = -8
b) (-1.5, -12.5)

Page 44 — Harder Graphs

Q1 **a)** (iii) **d)** (i)
b) (iv) **e)** (v)
c) (vi) **f)** (ii)

Q2

x	-3	-2	-1	0	1	2	3
x^3	-27	-8	-1	0	1	8	27
+4	4	4	4	4	4	4	4
y	-23	-4	3	4	5	12	31

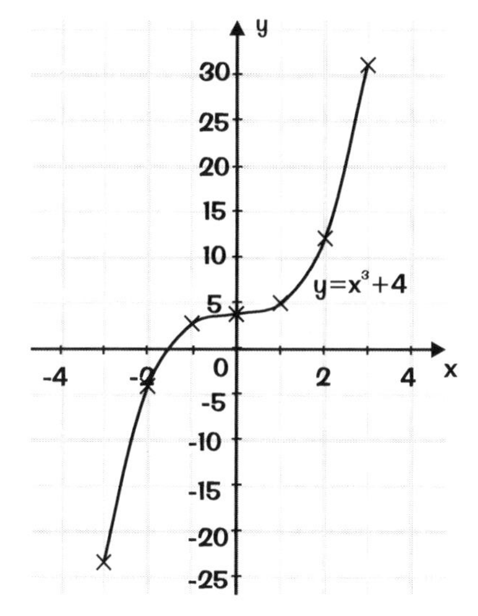

Q3

x	-3	-2	-1	0	1	2	3
$-x^3$	27	8	1	0	-1	-8	-27
+3	+3	+3	+3	+3	+3	+3	+3
y	30	11	4	3	2	-5	-24

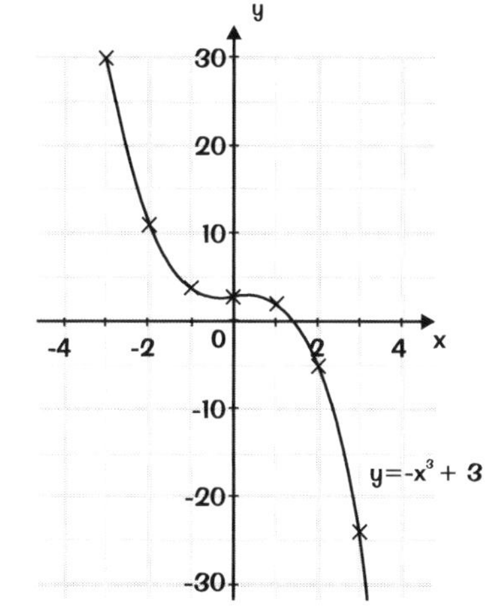

Q4

x	-4	-3	-2	-1	0	1	2	3	4
$y=1/x$	-0.25	-0.33	-0.5	-1	n/a	1	0.5	0.33	0.25

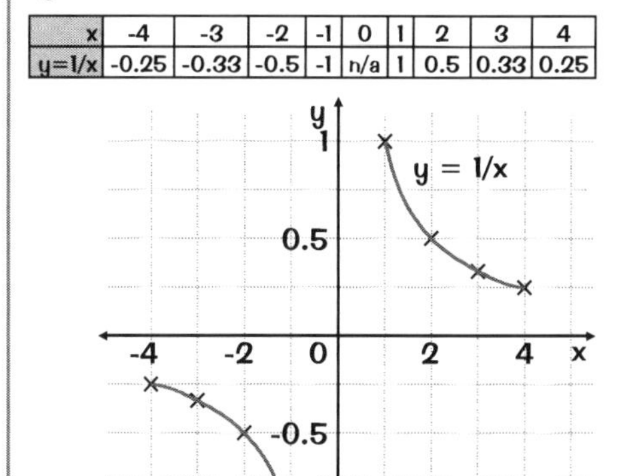

Answers: P45 — P50

Page 45 — Solving Equations Using Graphs

Q1 $x = 2, y = 3$
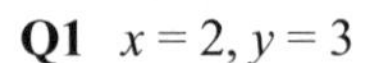

Q2 $x = 4$

Q3 **a)**
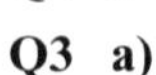
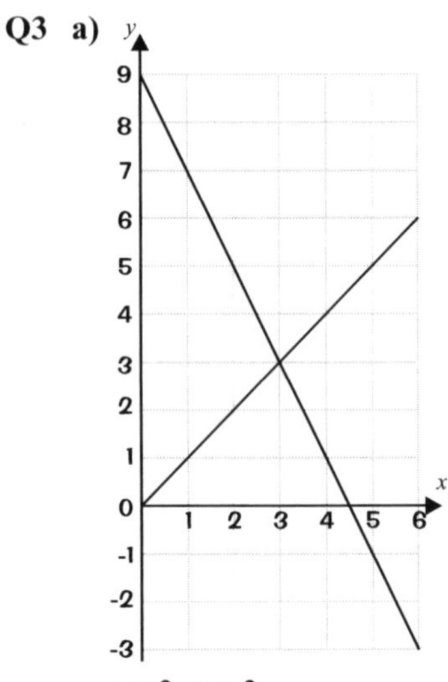

$x = 3, y = 3$

b)
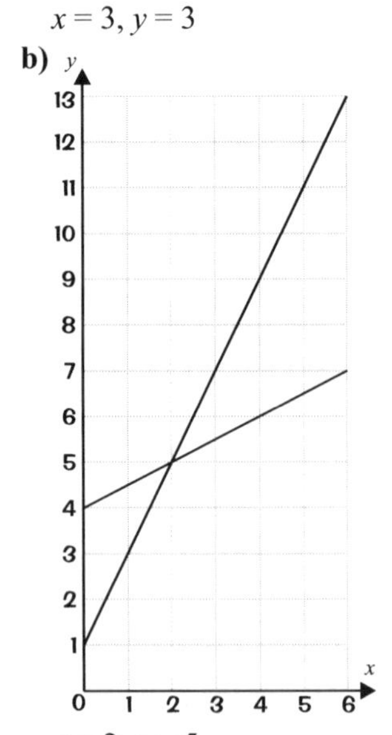

$x = 2, y = 5$

c)
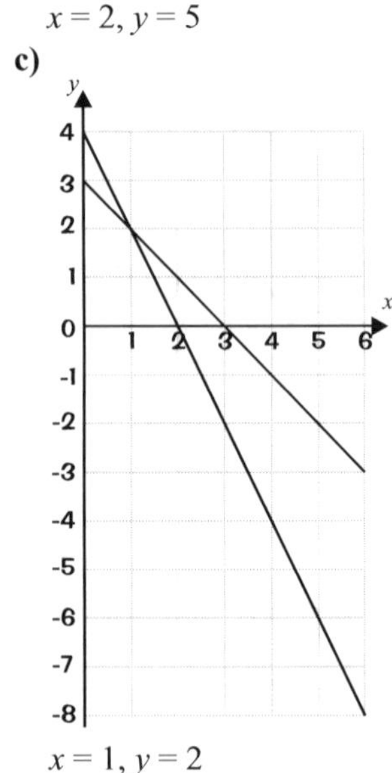

$x = 1, y = 2$

d)
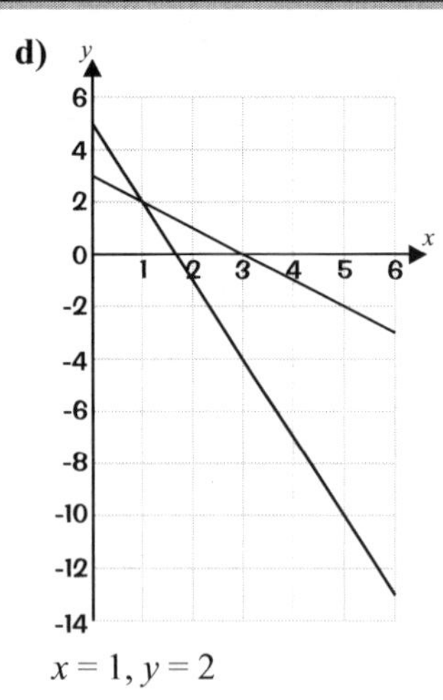

$x = 1, y = 2$

Q4 **a)** $x = -4$ and $x = 2$
b) $x = -3$ and $x = 1$

Page 46 — Distance-Time Graphs

Q1 **a)** 1:00 pm **b)** 30 km
c) 30 mins **d)** E
e) 45 mins **f)** 80 km/h

Q2 **a)** B **b)** 3 mins 45 secs
c) B
d) 267 m/min
e) C

Pages 47-48 — Real-Life Graphs

Q1 **a)** £5
b) £9.50
c) £17
d) No (Each 4.5 mile journey costs more than £8)

Q2
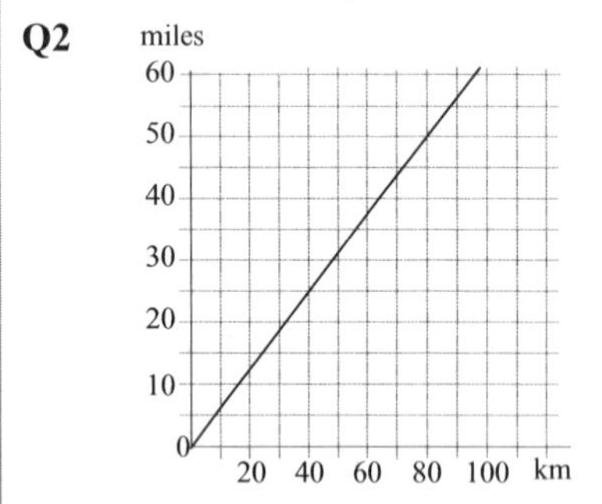

a) 12-13 miles
b) 43-44 miles
c) 56-57 miles

Q3 **a)** 63-65 km
b) 15-17 km
c) 47-49 km

Q4 **a)** 3 adults
b) £40

Q5 1 D 2 B
3 A 4 E
5 C

Q6 **a)**
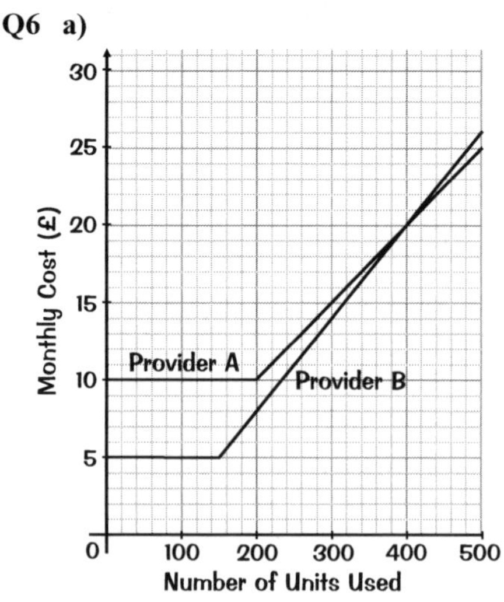

b) **i)** Provider A: £12.50
Provider B: £11

ii) Provider A: £23
Provider B: £23.60 (answers between £23.50 and £24 are acceptable)

c) 400 units

Section Four — Ratio, Proportion and Rates of Change

Pages 49-51 — Ratios

Q1 **b)** $5:7$
c) $8:5$
d) $2:3$
e) $7:40$
f) $21:68$
g) $2.9:8.7 = 29:87 = 1:3$
h) $\frac{3}{5}:\frac{9}{10} = \frac{6}{10}:\frac{9}{10} = 6:9 = 2:3$

Q2 **b)** $1:7$
c) $1:6.5$
d) $1:37.5$

Q3 **b)** $3.8:1$
c) $8.5:1$
d) $20:1$

Q4 **a)** 10 litres
b) 20 litres
c) 35 litres

Q5 **a)** 25 ml
b) 75 ml
c) 105 ml

Q6 **a)** 5500
b) 23265

Q7 **a)** **i)** There are $\frac{2}{5}$ as many cats as dogs.

ii) There are $\frac{5}{2}$ times as many dogs as cats.

Answers: P50 — P57

b) i) There are $\frac{3}{4}$ as many sprouts as peas.

ii) There are $\frac{4}{3}$ as many peas as sprouts.

Q8 $\frac{1}{2}$

Q9 a) $\frac{4}{11}$

b) 4 : 7

c) 32

Q10 a) £39

b) £140

Q11 a) 1 + 4 = 5
100 g ÷ 5 = 20 g
1 × 20 g = 20 g
4 × 20 g = 80 g
20 g : 80 g

b) 200 m : 300 m

c) £4000 : £8000

d) 2.7 kg : 3.6 kg

e) £3.60 : £4.50

Q12 a) £4000

b) Paul, £16

c) 3 km, 4.5 km, 7.5 km

Q13 The area of the triangle is 12 cm^2. Square area : triangle area = 4 : 3 = 16 : 12, so the area of the square is 16 cm^2 and its side length is 4 cm.

Q14 3 parts – 2 parts = 1 part is worth 2 animals. Fish make up 6 parts, so there are 2 × 6 = 12 fish.

Q15 a) 1 : 4 : 6

b) 4 parts – 1 part = 3 parts = £9, so 1 part = £3. Peggy's money makes up 6 parts, so she has 3 × 6 = £18.

Pages 52-53 — Direct Proportion Problems

Q1 £1.60

Q2 a) 400 g

b) 300 g

c) She will need 350 g of butter so she doesn't have enough.

Q3 a) 1.5625

b) 2.5

c) The larger bar

Q4 The smaller box

Q5 The 30 g bag gives you:
30 ÷ 65 = 0.46 g per penny.
The 160 g bag gives you:
160 ÷ 255 = 0.63 g per penny.
The 250 g bag gives you:
250 ÷ 349 = 0.72 g per penny.
So the 250 g bag represents the best value for money.

Q6 5

Q7 15 women = $\frac{5}{9}$
(15 ÷ 5) × 9 = 27 members in total.
So there are 12 men.

Q8 Cost for 1 child for 3 months = £408 ÷ 4 = £102
Cost for 1 child for 1 month = £102 ÷ 3 = £34
Cost for 3 children for 5 months = £34 × 3 × 5 = £510

Q9 He has 4 × 7 = 28 cups of tea.
He uses 28 × 50 = 1400 ml of milk and 28 teabags. The weekly teabags cost: (3 ÷ 140) × 28 = £0.60.
The milk costs
(55 ÷ 500) × 1400 = 154p = £1.54
£1.54 + £0.60 = £2.14

Q10 a) $y = 4x$

b) E.g.

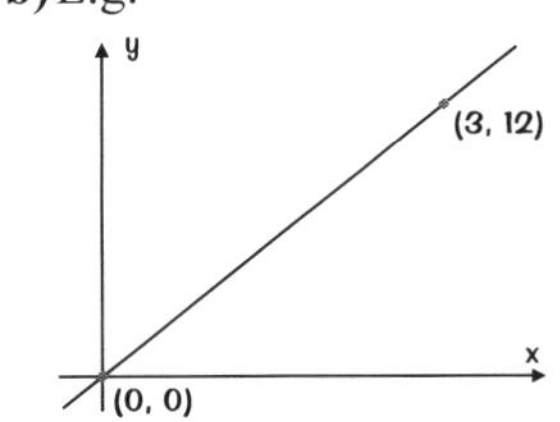

Q11 E.g.

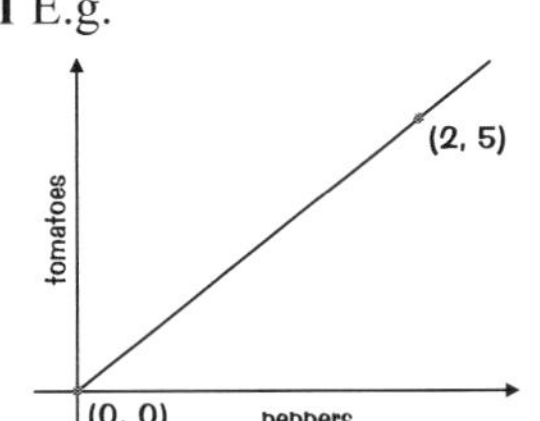

Page 54 — Inverse Proportion Problems

Q1 $y = \frac{1}{x}$, $\frac{1}{x} = \frac{y}{3}$, $x = \frac{8}{y}$

Q2 a) If a is multiplied by 3 then b is divided by 3.

b) If a is divided by 5 then b is multiplied by 5.

Q3 a) 3

b)

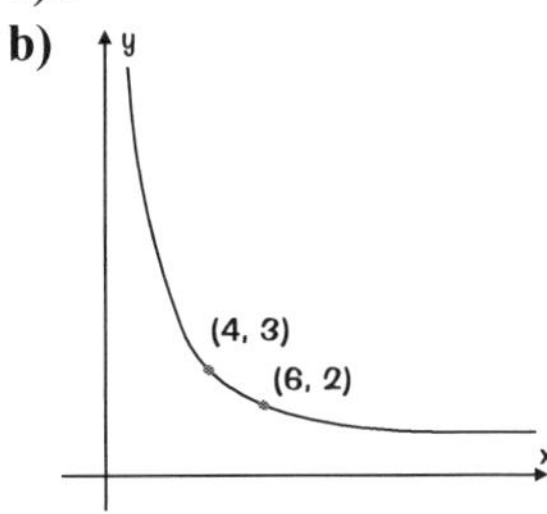

Q4 2 hours

Q5 It would take 3 people 12 hours, so 3 hours longer.

Q6

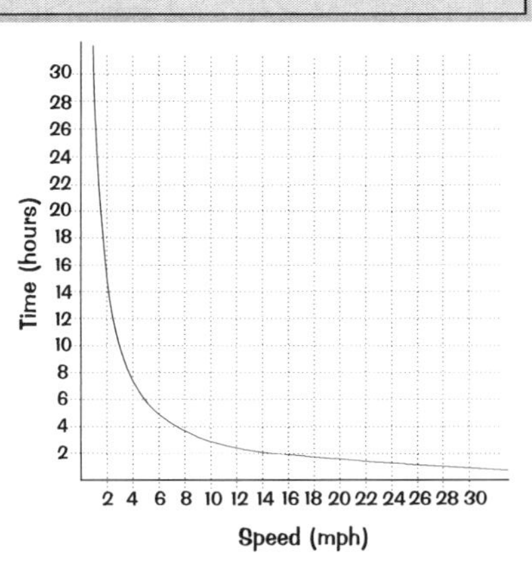

Pages 55-57 — Percentages

Q1 a) £5 **b)** £2.50
c) £15 **d)** 4.829 kg
e) £1.28 **f)** 629 kg
g) 54 mins

Q2 a) 44% **b)** 420
c) 60

Q3 Taxable Pay = £8300
a) £1660
b) £3320

Q4 a) 50% **b)** 25%
c) 80% **d)** 25%
e) 8% **f)** 38%

Q5 a) 40%
b) 5%
c) 125%

Q6 £1068

Q7 a) £49.90
b) £52

Q8 £5980

Q9 Car 1 costs £8495 – (0.15 × £8495) = £8495 – £1274.25 = £7220.75.
Car 2 costs £8195 – (0.12 × £8195) = £8195 – £983.40 = £7211.60.
So car 2 is the cheapest.

Q10 £15

Q11 12%

Q12 8.7%

Q13 a) Saved £10 of £45 = 22.2%
b) Saved £2 of £14.99 = 13.3%
c) Saved £4.75 of £27.50 = 17.3%

Q14 £80

Q15 300

Q16 75 cm is 15%, so 1% = 5 cm
Original height = 100% = 500 cm = 5 m

Q17 2013 salary
= 23 000 × 0.97 = £22 310
2014 salary
= £22 310 × 1.12 = £24 987.20
% increase = $\frac{1987.20}{23\,000} \times 100 = 8.64\%$

Q18 £67.80

Answers: P57 — P67

Q19 53%

Q20 48%

Page 58 — Compound Growth and Decay

Q1 £155

Q2 204

Q3 **a)** £145 800
b) 2 years

Q4 £108.04

Q5 **a)** £550
b) £244.04

Q6 £434 000

Q7 £585.26

Pages 59-60 — Unit Conversions

Q1 22, 35.2, 165
22.5, 63, 180

Q2 2 cm, 60 mm, 3.47 km, 2000 m
300 000 cm, 3400 mm, 8.55 kg,
1200 ml, 4.4 l

Q3 2 bags

Q4 94 inches

Q5 112 lbs, 40 ounces, 8.5 stone,
5 gallons, 60 feet, 3.2 feet

Q6 **a)** £4.69
b) £43.77
c) £341.50
d) The British courier

Q7 Tom by 1 km (or 0.625 miles).

Q8 4 km/h

Q9 **a)** Yes (1 gallon ≈ 4.5 litres)
b) No
c) 0.67 pints (to 2 d.p.)

Page 61 — Area and Volume Conversions

Q1 **a)** $900 \div 10 \div 10 = 9$ cm^2
b) $4 \times 100 \times 100 = 40\,000$ cm^2
c) $500 \div 100 \div 100 = 0.05$ m^2
d) $38.2 \times 10 \times 10 = 3820$ mm^2
e) $8.5 \times 1000 \times 1000 = 8\,500\,000$ m^2
f) $150\,000 \div 1000 \div 1000$
$= 0.15$ km^2

Q2 **a)** $4 \times 10 \times 10 \times 10 = 4000$ mm^3
b) $3 \times 100 \times 100 \times 100$
$= 3\,000\,000$ cm^3
c) $32\,500 \div 10 \div 10 \div 10 = 32.5$ cm^3
d) $55\,000 \div 100 \div 100 \div 100$
$= 0.055$ m^3
e) $25.1 \times 10 \times 10 \times 10 =$
$25\,100$ mm^3
f) $8.3 \times 100 \times 100 \times 100$
$= 8\,300\,000$ cm^3

Q3 $172 \times 100 \times 100 \times 100 =$
$172\,000\,000$ cm^3

Q4 0.12 m^2, yes.

Q5 300 000 mm^3
$= 300\,000 \div 10 \div 10 \div 10 = 300$ cm^3
For 3 cups, Mandy needs:
$300 \times 3 = 900$ cm^3 of water.
So Mandy does not have enough water in her kettle.

Page 62 — Time Intervals

Q1 14 400 seconds

Q2 3 minutes 32 seconds

Q3 **a)** 3 hours 45 mins
b) 12 mins
c) 5 hours 48 mins

Q4 1 hour 20 minutes

Q5 5 hours 15 mins

Q6 11:55 am
[(25 + 5.5 × 40) = 4 hours 5 mins]

Q7 **a)** Train 3
b) Train 1
c) 12:08

Page 63 — Speed

Q1 165 miles

Q2

Distance Travelled	Time taken	Average Speed
210 km	3 hrs	70 km/h
135 miles	4 hrs 30 mins	30 mph
105 km	2 hrs 30 mins	42 km/h
9 miles	45 mins	12 mph
640 km	48 mins	800 km/h
70 miles	1 hr 10 mins	60 mph

Q3 2 minutes 5 seconds

Q4 **a)** $100 \div 11 = 9.09$ m/s (to 2 d.p.)
b) 32.73 km/h (to 2 d.p.)

Q5 **a)** 32 minutes
b) 1200 m ÷ 56 seconds
= 21.428... m/s
(21.428... ÷ 1000) × 60 × 60
= 77.142... km/h
(77.142... ÷ 1.6) = 48.2 mph (1 d.p.)
So Simon was **not** speeding.

Page 64 — Density and Pressure

Q1 **a)** 0.75 g/cm^3
b) 0.8 g/cm^3

Q2 **a)** 62.4 g
b) 96 g

Q3 **a)** 625 cm^3
b) 89.3 cm^3 (to 1 d.p.)

Q4 3744 g (3.744 kg)

Q5 1.2 g/cm^3

Q6 0.93 g/cm^3

Q7 150 N/m^2

Q8 0.8 m^2

Q9 460.8 N

Section Five — Shapes and Area

Pages 65-67 — Properties of 2D Shapes

Q1 a) b) c)

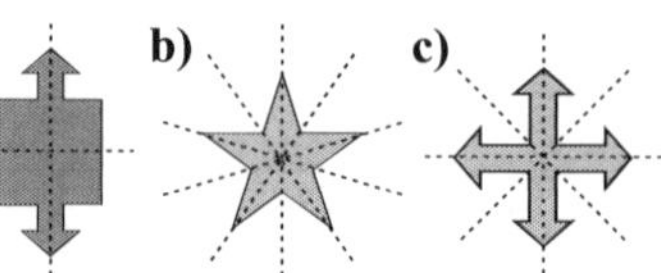

Q2 E.g.

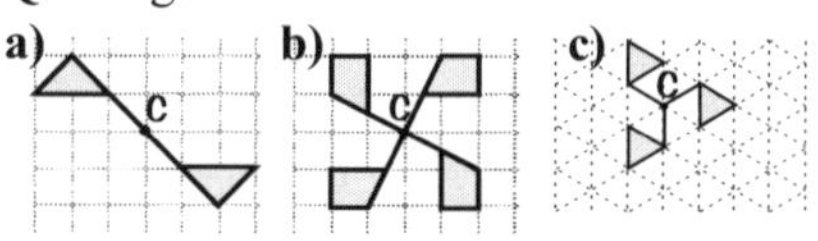

Q3 **a)** Regular octagon
Lines of symmetry = 8
Order of rotational symmetry = 8
b) Regular pentagon
Lines of symmetry = 5
Order of rotational symmetry = 5
c) Equilateral triangle
Lines of symmetry = 3
Order of rotational symmetry = 3
d) Regular hexagon
Lines of symmetry = 6
Order of rotational symmetry = 6
e) Regular heptagon
Lines of symmetry = 7
Order of rotational symmetry = 7

Q4 **a)** 2, 2
b) equilateral
c) no, no
d) right-angled
e) less/smaller, 90
f) obtuse-angled

Q5 E.g.

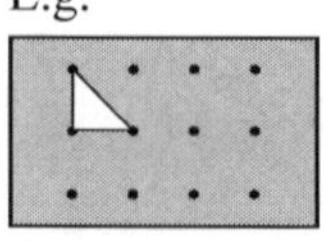
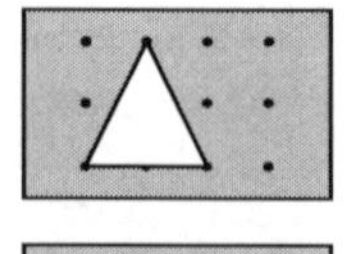
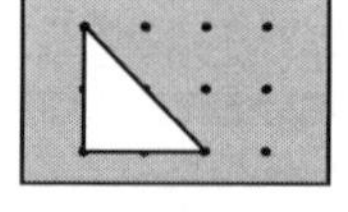
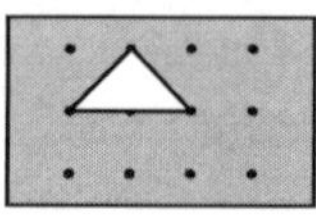

Q6 E.g.

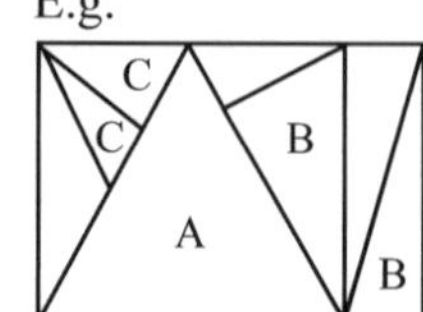

A = equilateral
B = right
C = scalene

Q7 12, scalene

Q8 Missing words (reading down):
Rectangle, parallelogram, parallel, two, equal
Missing drawings: E.g.

Answers: P67 — P74

Q9 Parallelograms have two pairs of equal angles, so one of the missing angles will be 52°.
Sum of interior angles = 360°
So two interior angles
= 360° – (2 × 52°) = 256°
256° ÷ 2 = 128°
So the three other angles will be 52°, 128° and 128°.

Page 68 — Congruent Shapes

Q1 a

Q2 **a)** ABC and DFE are congruent by SAS (two sides and the angle between them are the same).
b) ABC and GHI are congruent by AAS (two angles and a corresponding side are the same).
c) DEF and GHI are congruent by RHS (a right angle, the hypotenuse and one other side match up).

Q3 E.g. Sides AB and CD are the same, sides AM and CM are the same and sides BM and DM are the same (as M is the midpoint of the diagonals). So triangles ABM and CDM are congruent by SSS (all three sides are the same length).

Page 69 — Similar Shapes

Q1 A, D and E

Q2 **a)** No — the scale factors are different
$\frac{2}{3} \neq \frac{5.5}{9}$
b) Yes — the two labelled sides are proportional and the angle between them is the same.

Q3 **a)** 75°
b) Scale factor = 3, so GH = 9 cm

Q4 Larger shape scale factor = 2
Area of large shape = 10 × 12
= 120 m^2
Smaller shape scale factor = 3
Area of small shape = 6 × 9
= 54 m^2
So shaded area = 66 m^2

Q5 **a)** Angle A shared. Parallel lines make corresponding angles equal so the triangles are similar as all three angles are the same.
b) Scale factor = $\frac{AD}{AB} = \frac{20}{12} = \frac{5}{3}$
So $x = 25 \div \frac{5}{3} = 15$ cm
Also $y + 10 = \frac{5}{3}y$
=> $2y = 30$, $y = 15$ cm

Page 70 — Transformations — Translations

Q1

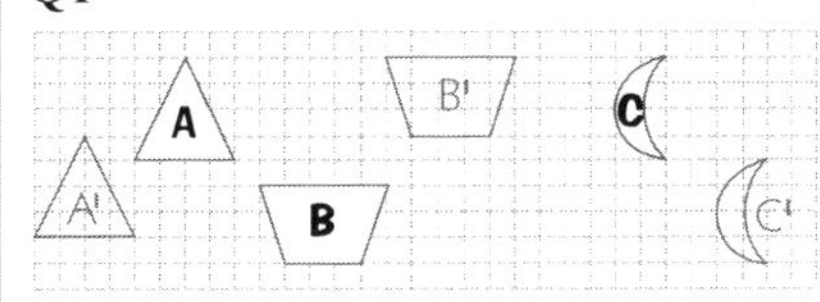

Q2

Q3 **a)** S $\xrightarrow{\binom{5}{2}}$ S_1
b) T $\xrightarrow{\binom{0}{-5}}$ T_1
c) R $\xrightarrow{\binom{-4}{-3.5}}$ R_1

Page 71 — Transformations — Rotations

Q1 P' (-4, 3), Q' (0, 5), R' (-1, 0)

Q2 **a)**, **b)**, **d)**, **e)** — see diagram

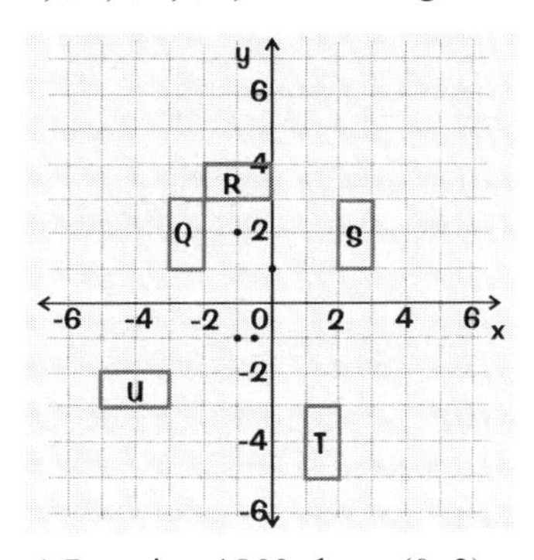

c) Rotation 180° about (0, 2).
f) 90° rotation anticlockwise about $\left(-\frac{1}{2}, -\frac{1}{2}\right)$, or 90° rotation clockwise about (-2, -6).

Page 72 — Transformations — Reflections

Q1

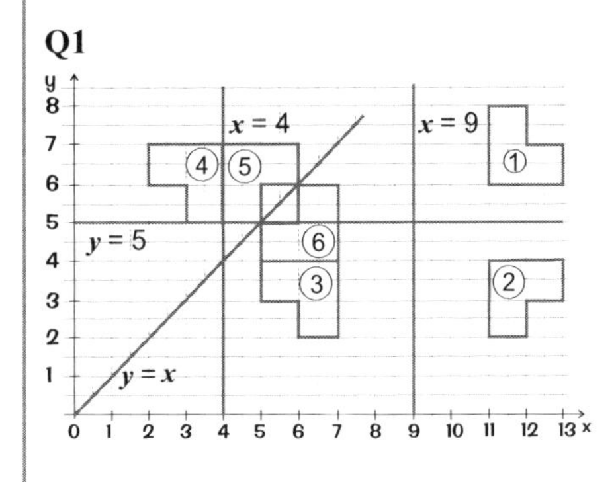

Q2 **a)** and **b)**

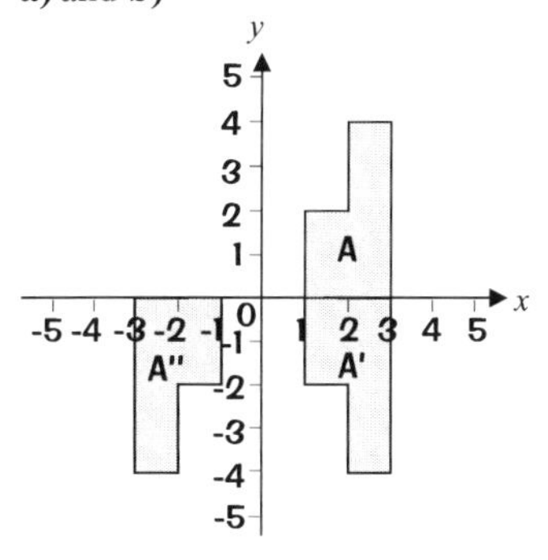

c) Rotation through 180°, about the origin.

Q3 **a)** $y = 4.5$
b) $x = 0.5$
c) $y = x$

Page 73 — Transformations — Enlargements

Q1

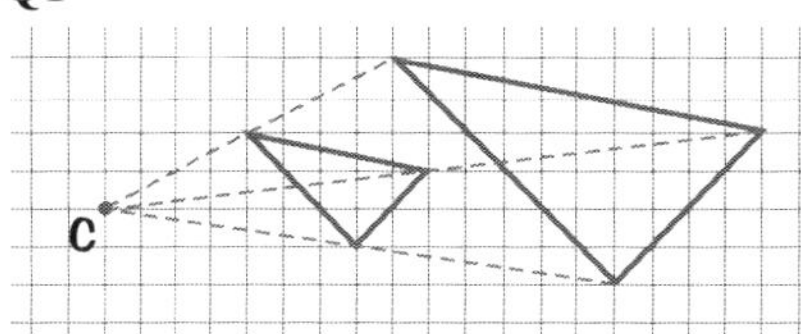

Q2 **a)** **A:** 3 **B:** 2 **C:** 3
b) Centres of enlargement marked:

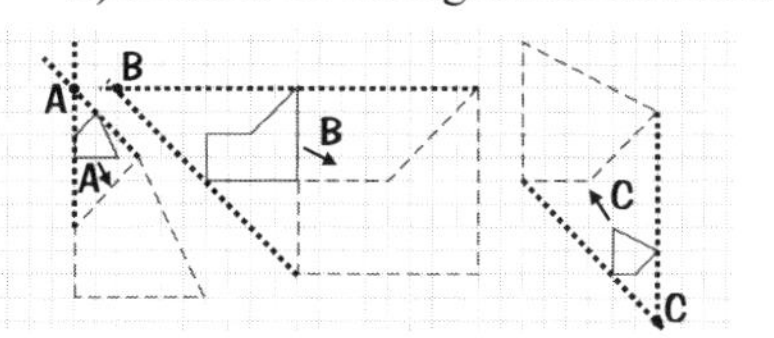

Q3

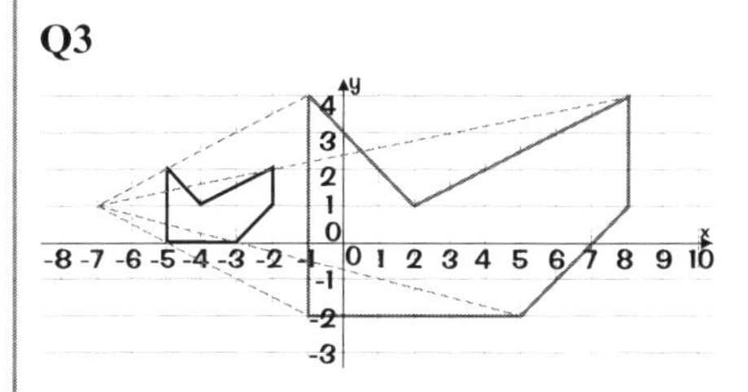

Pages 74-76 — Perimeter and Area

Q1 **a)** 76 cm
b) 72 cm

Q2 **a)** 68 m
b) 68 ÷ 5 = 13.6, so 14 rolls needed

Q3 **a)** 40 cm^2
b) 1045 cm^2
c) 4340 m^2
d) 5.55 km^2

Q4 Room 1 = 4.8 × 3.9 = 18.72 m^2
Room 2 = 4.2 × 3.1 = 13.02 m^2
Total area of carpet needed
= 18.72 + 13.02 = 31.74 m^2

Answers: P74 — P81

Q5 **a)** 54 cm^2
b) 7.5 cm^2
c) 87.5 m^2
d) 5.12 m^2

Q6 Area of small triangle
$= \frac{1}{2} \times 15 \times 15 = 112.5$ cm^2
Area of larger triangle
$= \frac{1}{2} \times 15 \times 35 = 262.5$ cm^2
Total area
$= 112.5 + 112.5 + 262.5 + 262.5$
$= 750$ cm^2

Q7 Base length $= 4773 \div 43 = 111$ mm

Q8 Area of metal blade
$= \frac{1}{2} \times 35 \times (70 + 155)$
$= 3937.5$ mm^2

Q9 **a)** $48 \div 5 = 9.6$ m long
b) Area of 1 roll $= 11$ m $\times 0.5$ m
$= 5.5$ m^2.
48 $m^2 \div 5.5$ $m^2 = 8.73$ rolls, so 9 rolls should be ordered.

Q10 Width of rectangle = 4 m.
So perimeter $= 10 + 4 + 10 + 4$
$= 28$ m.

Q11 Area of square $= 3^2 = 9$ cm^2.
Area of triangle $= 0.5 \times 3 \times$ height
So $1.5 \times$ height $= 9$, which means the height of the triangle = 6 cm.

Q12 **a)** Shape A:
Area $= 15 \times 10 = 150$ cm^2
Shape B:
Area $= 5 \times 4 = 20$ cm^2
Total $= 150 + 20 = 170$ cm^2
b) Area of rectangle $= 20 \times 12$
$= 240$ cm^2
Area of triangle $= \frac{1}{2}(12 \times 5)$
$= 30$ cm^2
Shaded area $= 240 - 30$
$= 210$ cm^2
c) Area of rectangle $= 8 \times 6$
$= 48$ cm^2
Area of triangle $= \frac{1}{2}(14 \times 6)$
$= 42$ cm^2
Area of whole shape $= 48 + 42$
$= 90$ cm^2

Q13 $0.5 \times 1.5 = 0.75$ m^2
$1.5 \times 1.5 = 2.25$ m^2
Total Area $= (4 \times 0.75) + 2.25$
$= 5.25$ m^2
He needs to buy 6 bags of gravel.

Q14 **a)** Area of large white square
$= 5^2 = 25$ cm^2
Area of small grey square
$= 3.8^2 = 14.44$ cm^2
Area of four white triangles =
$25 - 14.44 = 10.56$ cm^2
Area of one white triangle =
$10.56 \div 4 = 2.64$ cm^2.
b) Area of white triangle =
$0.5 \times 3.8 \times x = 2.64$
$x = 1.4$ cm to 1 d.p.

Pages 77-78 — Perimeter and Area — Circles

Q1 B = major sector
C = chord
D = tangent

Q2 **a)** Circumference = 6.28 cm
Area = 3.14 cm^2
b) Diameter = 5 cm
Circumference = 15.71 cm
Area = 19.63 cm^2

Q3 8836 cm^2

Q4 1.88 m

Q5 **a)** 113.10 m^2 (to 2 d.p.)
b) 2262 ml

Q6 $C = \pi \times D = \pi \times 0.64$ m
$= 2.0106...$ m
So distance travelled =
$2.0106... \times 100 = 201$ m

Q7 **a)** Circumference of full circle
$= 6\pi$ cm
Arc length $= \frac{240}{360} \times 6\pi = 4\pi$ cm
b) Area of full circle $= 81\pi$ cm
Area of sector $= \frac{120}{360} \times 81\pi$
$= 27\pi$ m^2

Q8 **a)** **i)** Circumference of full circle
$= 20\pi$ cm
Length of curve $= \frac{60}{360} \times 20\pi$
$= \frac{10\pi}{3}$ cm $= 10.47$ cm
ii) $10 + 10 + 10.47 = 30.47$ cm
b) Area of full circle
$= \pi \times 10^2 = 100\pi$
Area of drawn shape
$= \frac{60}{360} \times 100\pi = \frac{50\pi}{3}$ cm
$= 52.36$ cm^2

Q9 Area of white portion of tile
= area of whole tile – area of four quarter circles
$= 7^2 - 4 \times \left(\frac{1}{4} \times \pi \times 3^2\right)$
$= 20.73$ cm^2 to 2 d.p.

Page 79-80 — 3D Shapes — Surface Area

Q1 **a)** Cylinder
b) Cone
c) Sphere
d) Cube
e) Square-based pyramid
f) Cuboid
g) Triangular prism
h) Regular tetrahedron (triangle-based pyramid)

Q2 **a)** 8
b) 6
c) 12

Q3 **a)** Area of triangular face
$= \frac{1}{2} \times 5 \times 4$
$= 10$ cm^2
Area of square base $= 4 \times 4$
$= 16$ cm^2
Total surface area $= 16 + (4 \times 10)$
$= 56$ cm^2
b) Area of triangular face
$= \frac{1}{2} \times 3 \times 4$
$= 6$ cm^2
Areas of rectangular faces are:
1) $4 \times 2 = 8$ cm^2
2) $3 \times 2 = 6$ cm^2
3) $5 \times 2 = 10$ cm^2
Total surface area
$= (2 \times 6) + 8 + 6 + 10$
$= 36$ cm^2

Q4 **a)** Area of each isosceles triangle
$= \frac{1}{2} \times 2.3 \times 3.2 = 3.68$ m^2
b) Area of each side $= 3.4 \times 4$
$= 13.6$ m^2
c) Groundsheet $= 2.3 \times 4 = 9.2$ m^2
d) Total material
$= 2 \times 3.68 + 9.2 + 2 \times 13.6$
$= 43.76$ m^2

Q5 **a)** 452.39 cm^2
b) 75.40 cm^2
c) 753.98 cm^2

Q6 900π cm^2

Q7 Surface area of container
$= 603.2$ cm^2, so Hannah doesn't have enough paper to wrap the perfume.

Pages 81-83 — 3D Shapes — Volume

Q1 140 cm^3

Q2 **a)** 125 cm^3
b) 729 m^3
c) 3375 mm^3

Q3 120 cm = 1.2 m, so volume of water needed $= 12 \times 18 \times 1.2 = 259.2$ m^3

Q4 **a)** 8 cm^3
b) Yes.
8 cm $\div$ 2 cm = 4,
12 cm $\div$ 2 cm = 6,
10 cm $\div$ 2 cm = 5,
so the container will hold
$4 \times 6 \times 5 = 120$ cubes.

Q5 **a)** $(30 \times 90) + [(60 + 30) \times 30]$
$= 5400$ cm^2
b) $5400 \times 100 = 540\,000$ cm^3

Q6 $(\frac{1}{2} \times 4 \times 3) \times 8 = 48$ cm^3

Answers: P82 — P91

Q7 **a)** 113.10 cm^3
b) 942.48 m^3

Q8 Volume = $\pi \times 0.3^2 \times 1.7$
= 0.48 m^3

Q9 **a)** 4188.79 mm^3
b) 37.70 cm^3
c) 2 468 666.67 m^3

Q10 Volume of volleyball
$= \frac{4}{3}\pi \times 9^3 = 972\pi$ cm^3
Volume of box
$= \pi \times 9^2 \times 18 = 1458\pi$ cm^3
So the ratio of the volumes is 2 : 3.

Q11 **a)** 18π cm^3
b) $\frac{2}{3}\pi$ cm^3
c) $17\frac{1}{3}\pi$ cm^3 (or $\frac{52}{3}\pi$ cm^3)

Q12 **a)** Volume of water when 25 cm deep = 150 × 200 × 25
= 750 000 cm^3
b) Time needed to fill pool to 25 cm
= 750 000 ÷ 50 000 = 15 mins

Q13 **a)** V = $3.14 \times 7^2 \times 9$
= 1384.74 cm^3
b) D = 1200 ÷ (49 π) = 7.79... cm
= 8 cm to nearest whole cm.

Page 84 — Projections

Q1

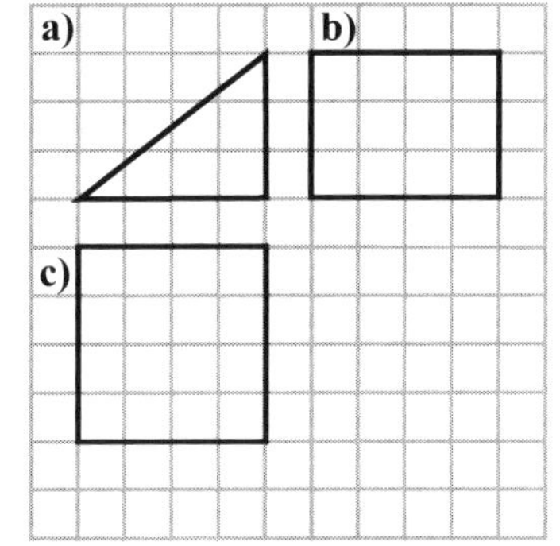

Q2 30

Q3

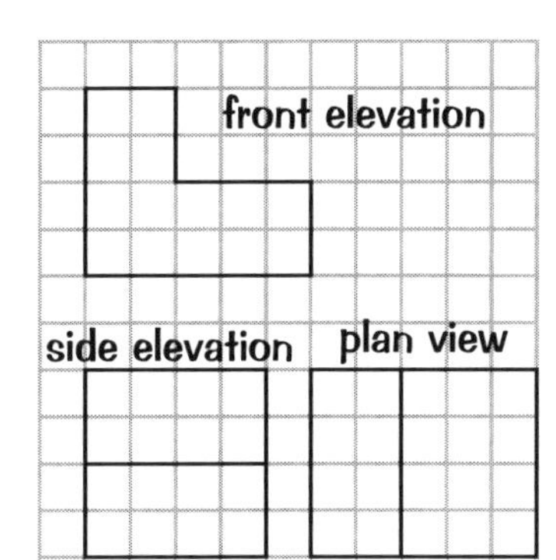

Q4

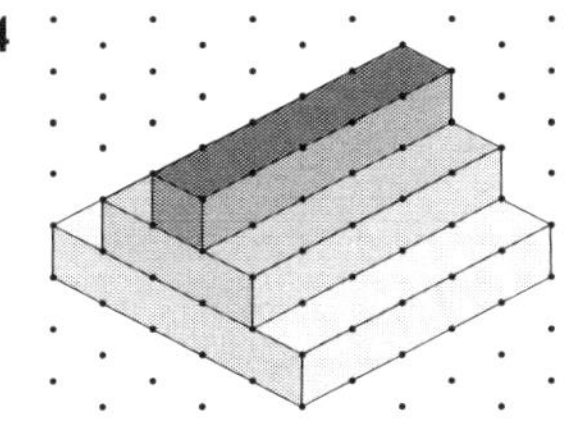

Section Six — Angles and Geometry

Pages 85-86 — Angle Basics

Q1 **a)** 90° **b)** 180°
c) 270° **d)** 360°

Q2 **b)** obtuse, 143°
c) right, 90°
d) reflex, 301°
e) reflex, 248°
f) acute, 16°

Q3 a = 60° b = 104°
c = 95° d = 42°
e = 139° f = 41°
g = 86°

Q4 110° 35°
60° 30°

Q5 80° 60°

Q6 a = 54° b = 63° c = 101°

Q7 **a)** QRP = 60°. Angles in a straight line add to 180°.
b) RPQ = 180 – 60 – 45 = 75°.
c) 360° (as they do at any point).

Page 87 — Parallel Lines

Q1 **a)** and **b)**

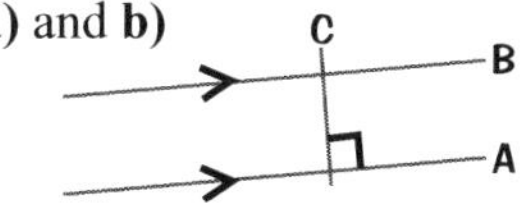

Q2 a = 130° corresponding
b = 56° allied
c = 48° alternate
d = 72° alternate
e = 50° alternate
f = 65° corresponding
g = 46° allied
h = 75° alternate
i = 119° allied
j = 61° corresponding

Q3 $x = 13°$

Page 88 — Geometry Problems

Q1 The third angle inside the triangle is 180° – 148° = 32°
So x = 180° – 32° – 70° = 78°

Q2 **a)** $3x$ = 180° – 42° – 63°
$3x$ = 75°
x = 25°
b) Angle ADC = 180° – $2x$ – 90°
= 40°
c) All the angles in triangle ACD are different, so it is not isosceles.

Q3 x = 180° – 75° – 47° = 58°
Angle ABC = x – 25° + x = 91°
Angle CEA
= 360° – 91° – 92° – 47° = 130°

Q4 **a)** Angles CBE and BEF are alternate angles so angle BEF = 46°.
b) Angles AFD and CDF are allied angles, so angle AFD = 180° – 104° = 76°.
c) Angle BFE = 76° – 30° = 46°
So triangle BEF has two angles that are both 46°.
So BEF is an isosceles triangle.

Pages 89-90 — Angles in Polygons

Q1 A regular polygon is a many sided shape where all the side lengths and angles are the same.

Q2 **a)** 45°
b) 135°
c) 360°
d) 72°
e) 108°

Q3 **a)** 5 cm
b) Sum of interior angles
= (6 – 2) × 180°
= 720°
angle c = 720 ÷ 6 = 120°

Q4 **a)** Hexagon
b) Decagon
c) Nonagon

Q5 (7 – 2) × 180° = 900°

Q6 **a)** (6 – 2) × 180° = 720°
b) $x + x + 2(x + 20°) + 2(x + 40°)$
= 720°
$6x$ + 120° = 720°
$6x$ = 600°, x = 100°

Q7 The sum of the interior angles in each triangle is 180°. So the sum of the interior angles in the polygon is 180° × 4 = 720°

Pages 91-93 — Loci and Construction

Q1 AB = 55 or 56 mm

Q2

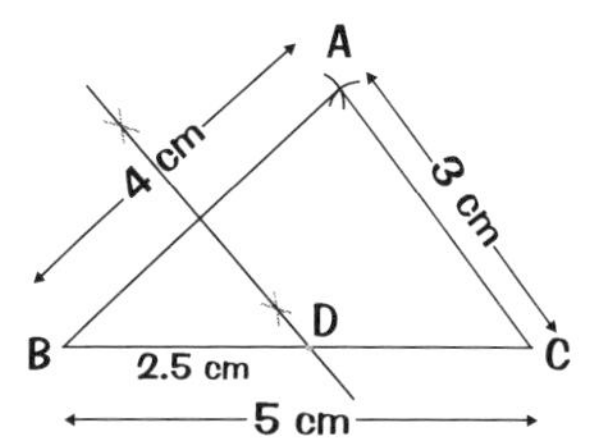

Q3

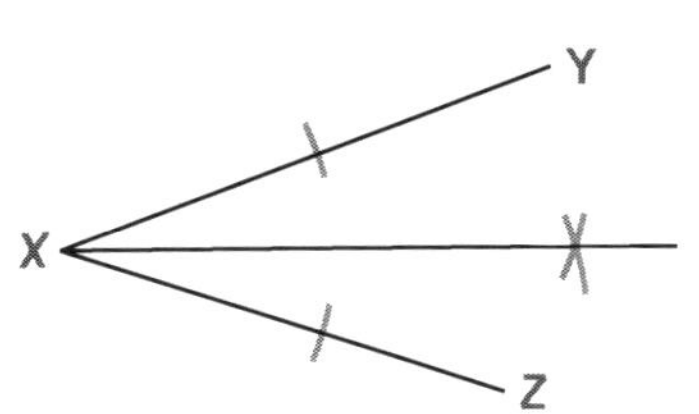

Answers: P91 — P99

Q4

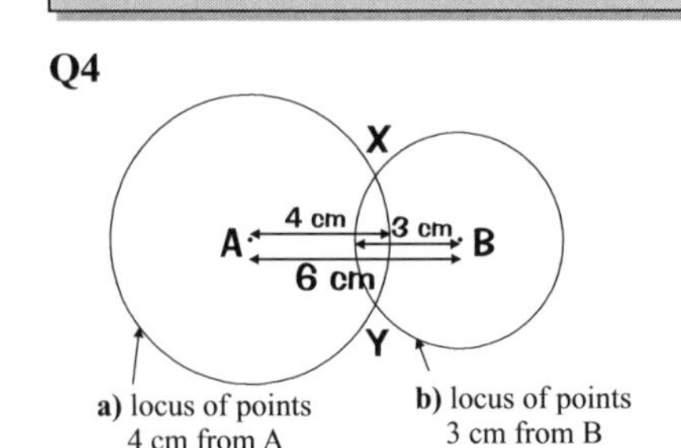

Q5

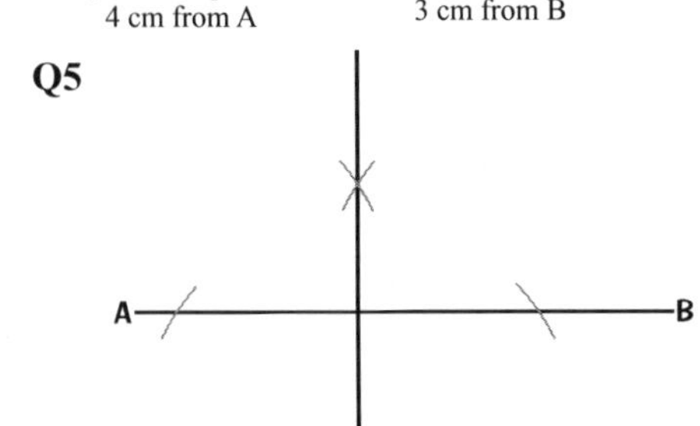

Q6

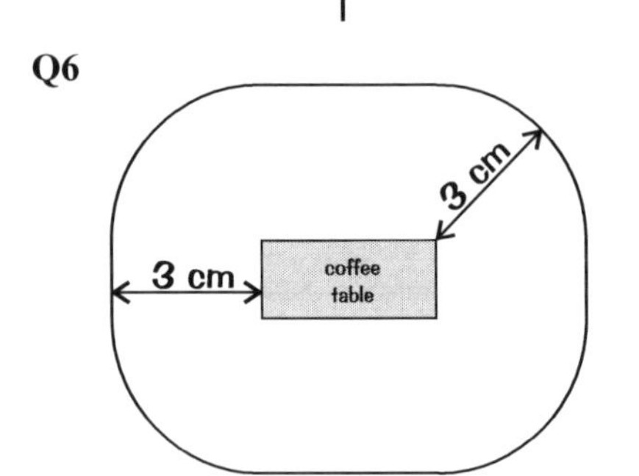

Q7

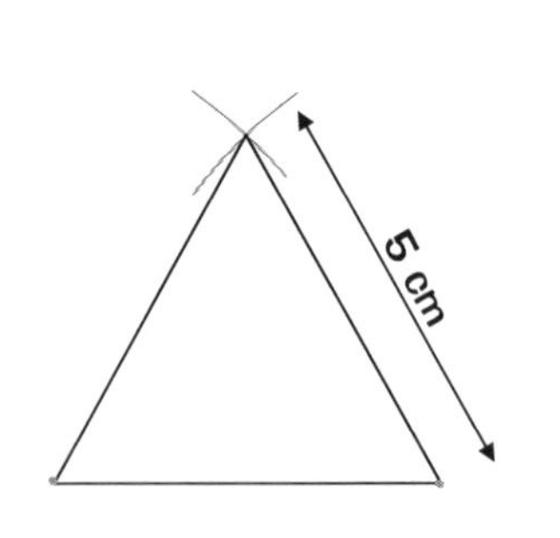

Q8

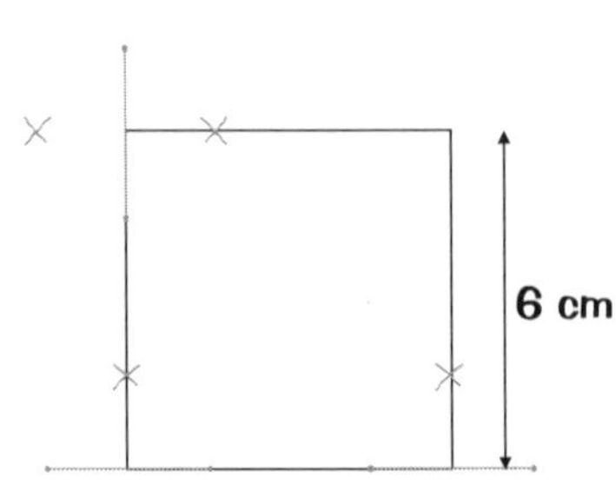

Q9 Area where house could go is shaded black:

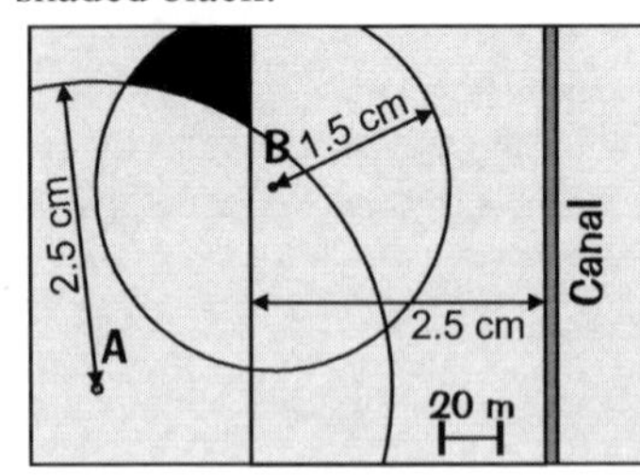

Q10

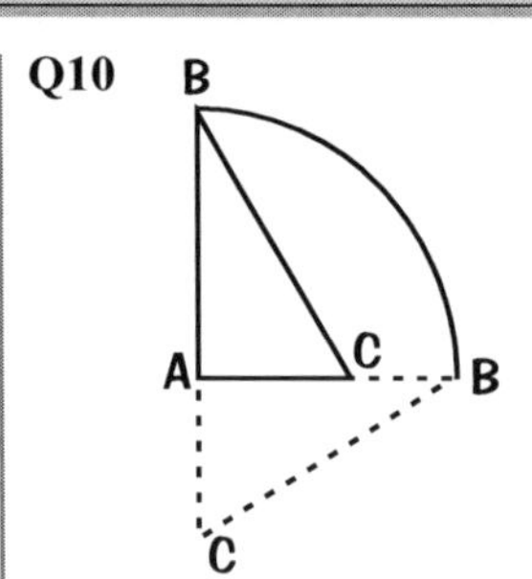

Page 94 — Bearings

Q1 122° to 126°

Q2 303° to 308°

Q3 **a)** 040° to 044°
b) 320° to 325°
c) 100° to 104°

Q4

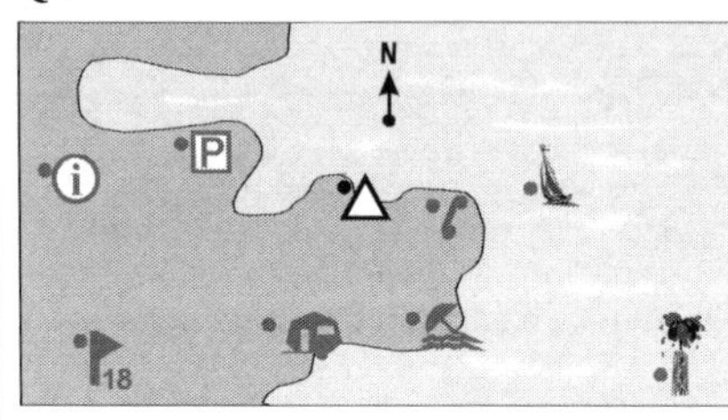

Q5 **a)** 245°
b) 310°
c) 035°

Pages 95-96 — Maps and Scale Drawings

Q1 **a)** 4.1 cm
b) 16.4 km
c) 53.2 km
d)

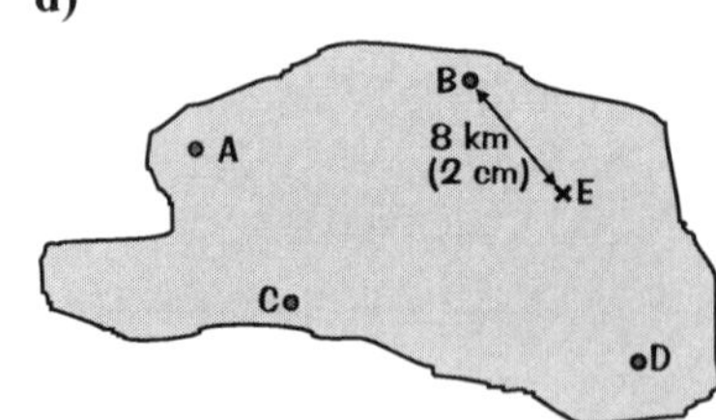

Q2 **a)** 13.8 m
b) Length: 1.95 m, width 2.6 m

Q3 Length: 10 cm, width: 7.5 cm

Q4 3 cm long, 2 cm wide

Q5 4 cm, 3 cm

E.g.

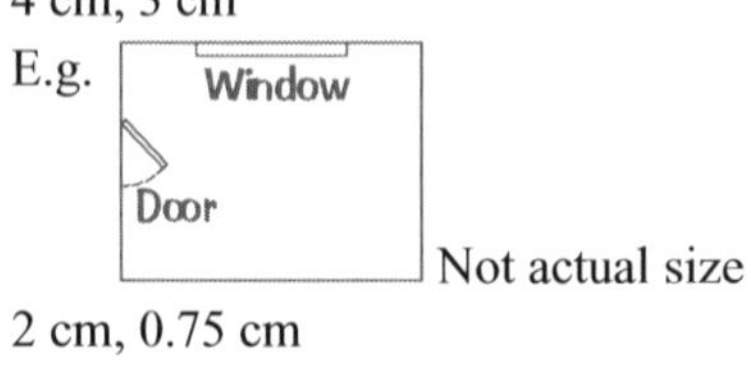

Not actual size

2 cm, 0.75 cm

Q6 **a)**

N
115°
85°
3 cm
Ryan's house
Petrol station
4 cm
Supermarket

b) 2 cm on map, so 10 km

Page 97 — Pythagoras' Theorem

Q1 c = 5 cm
d = 12 mm

Q2 A: $100 = 64 + 36$ Yes
B: $144 \neq 64 + 16$ No
C: $36 \neq 16 + 12.25$ No
D: $625 = 576 + 49$ Yes
So A and D are right angled.

Q3 e = 8 mm
f = 11.3 mm
g = h = 9.43 cm

Q4 9.5 m

Q5 6.4 cm

Page 98 — Trigonometry — Sin, Cos, Tan

Q1 a = 1.4 cm
$\theta = 28.1°$
b = 5.3 cm

Q2 c = 12.6 cm
d = 11.3 cm
$\theta = 49.5°$

Q3 e = 4.9 cm
$\theta = 52.4°$
f = 5.3 cm

Q4 $g = 15\sqrt{3}$ cm $\quad h = \frac{23\sqrt{3}}{2}$ cm
i = 9 cm

Q5 $\sin 30° + \tan 60° = \frac{1}{2} + \sqrt{3}$
$= \frac{1 + 2\sqrt{3}}{2}$

Page 99 — Vectors

Q1 **a)** $\begin{pmatrix} 1 \\ 9 \end{pmatrix}$
b) $\begin{pmatrix} 4 \\ 10 \end{pmatrix}$
c) $\begin{pmatrix} 3 \\ -12 \end{pmatrix}$
d) $\begin{pmatrix} 10 \\ 12 \end{pmatrix}$

Q2 $\mathbf{m} + \mathbf{n}$

Q3 **a)** $\mathbf{k} = 2\mathbf{j}$
$\mathbf{l} = \mathbf{j} - \mathbf{i}$
$\mathbf{m} = \mathbf{i} + \mathbf{j}$
b) $\mathbf{j} - 2\mathbf{i}$

Q4 **a)** $7\mathbf{s} + \mathbf{t}$
b) $-14\mathbf{s} - 2\mathbf{t}$

Answers: P100 — P106

Section Seven — Probability and Statistics

Page 100 — Probability Basics

Q1 a) Certain (unless there's a climate catastrophe)

b) Impossible (barring breakthroughs in medical technology)

c) Unlikely

Q2 a) & b)

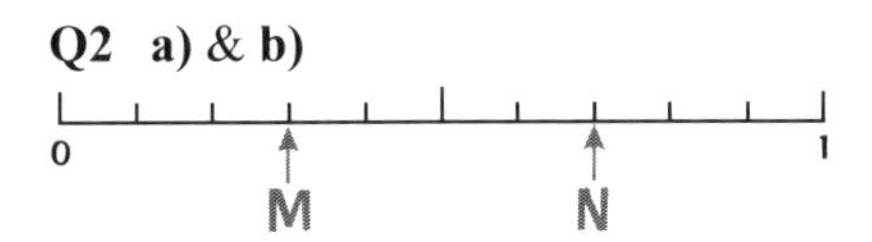

Q3 0.1

Q4 a) $\frac{3}{6} = \frac{1}{2}$, 0.5, 50%

b) $\frac{26}{52} = \frac{1}{2}$, 0.5, 50%

c) $\frac{2}{52} = \frac{1}{26}$, 0.038, 3.8%

Q5 a) $\frac{3}{10}$

b) $\frac{5}{10} = \frac{1}{2}$

c) $\frac{2}{10} = \frac{1}{5}$

d) $\frac{7}{10}$

e) 0

Page 101 — Listing Outcomes

Q1

		2nd COIN	
		H	T
1st COIN	H	HH	HT
	T	TH	TT

a) 4, **b)** $\frac{1}{4}$, **c)** $\frac{1}{4}$

Q2

		2nd DICE					
		1	2	3	4	5	6
1st DICE	1	2	3	4	5	6	7
	2	3	4	5	6	7	8
	3	4	5	6	7	8	9
	4	5	6	7	8	9	10
	5	6	7	8	9	10	11
	6	7	8	9	10	11	12

a) There are 36 ways of rolling the two dice.

b) i) $\frac{1}{36}$

ii) $\frac{5}{36}$

iii) $\frac{3}{36} = \frac{1}{12}$

iv) $\frac{6}{36} = \frac{1}{6}$

v) $\frac{3}{36} = \frac{1}{12}$

vi) 0

c) E.g. Scoring an odd number / scoring an even number.

Q3 a) 6

b) 2

c) 4

Page 102 — Probability Experiments

Q1 50 times

Q2 a)

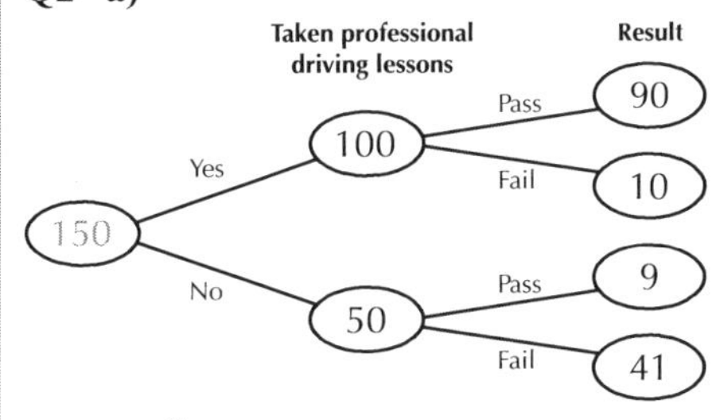

b) $\frac{9}{50} = 0.18$

Q3 a) 0.2

b)

Number	1	2	3	4	5
Number of times generated	18	19	22	21	20
Relative frequency	0.18	0.19	0.22	0.21	0.2

c) No, because all the relative frequencies are fairly close to the expected probability of 0.2.

d) i) They should all get closer and closer to 0.2.

ii) 20 000

Page 103 — The AND / OR Rules

Q1 a) 0.4

b) i) 0.36 **ii)** 0.16

Q2 a) 0.2 **b)** 0.65

c) 0.85

Q3 a) $\frac{26}{52} = \frac{1}{2}$

b) $\frac{13}{52} = \frac{1}{4}$

c) $\frac{1}{2} + \frac{1}{4} = \frac{3}{4}$

Q4 a) $\frac{1}{9}$

b) 0

c) $\frac{2}{9}$

Page 104 — Tree Diagrams

Q1 a) $0.6 \times 0.6 = 0.36$

b) $0.4 \times 0.4 = 0.16$

c) $0.6 \times 0.4 = 0.24$

d) $(0.4 \times 0.6) + (0.6 \times 0.4) = 0.48$

Q2 a)

Morning — Evening

Late (0.2): Late 0.7, On time 0.3

On time (0.8): Late 0.1, On time 0.9

b) $0.8 \times 0.9 = 0.72$

Page 105 — Sets and Venn Diagrams

Q1

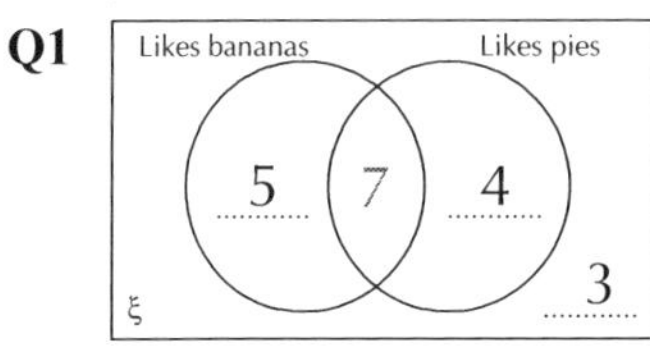

Q2 a)

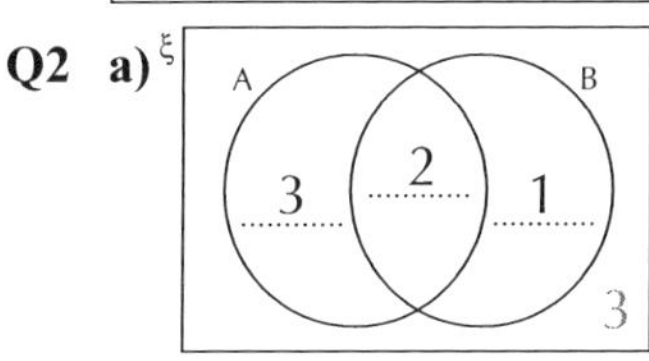

b) i) $\frac{5}{9}$

ii) $\frac{2}{9}$

iii) $\frac{6}{9} = \frac{2}{3}$

Q3 a)

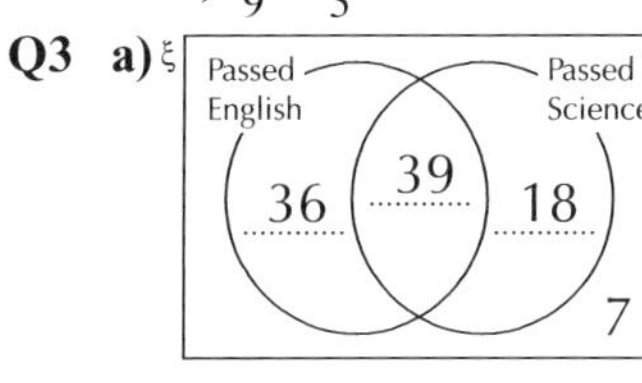

b) $\frac{54}{100} = 0.54$

Page 106 — Sampling and Bias

Q1 a) All 20- to 30-year-old women in the UK.

b) All football players in the Premier League.

Q2 a) All the residents in the surrounding area.

b) E.g. Any two answers from:

1. Their sample is made up of people who do their shopping at the same time (who might all have similar tastes).
2. Their sample is made up of people who already shop at Cheapeez — they also need to include some local residents who don't currently shop there.
3. Their sample is too small — they need to ask more people.

Answers: P106 — P112

Q3 a) Fred's sample is non-random. The people in it are likely to be commuters, so it doesn't fairly represent the whole population.
b) Fred should use a simple random sample – e.g. a random sample taken throughout the day, chosen from all public transport users in his town.

Q4 A computer or calculator could be used.

Page 107 — Collecting Data

Q1 a) Qualitative
b) Quantitative
c) Quantitative

Q2 a) Discrete
b) Continuous

Q3

Length of time (mins)	Tally	Frequency
1-10	卌	5
11-20	卌 |	6
21-30	||	2
31-40	||||	4
41-50	|||	3

Q4 a) There is no time period specified / the question is subjective – "very often" can mean different things to different people.
b) The question is ambiguous because the age classes overlap, e.g. someone who's 30 could go in either the 18-30 or 30-40 group.

Pages 108-109 — Mean, Median, Mode and Range

Q1 a) Mode = 3, Range = 6
b) Mode = 52, Range = 75

Q2 a) 2, 2, 3, 4, 5, 6, 7, 9, 12. Median is 5.
b) 2, 3, 5, 5, 7, 14, 19, 21. Median is 6.

Q3 a) 134, 134, 139, 146, 148, 149, 152, 156, 157, 158, 162, 163, 167, 172, 174. Median is 156 cm.
b) 40 cm

Q4 a) 12.5
b) 10
c) 70

Q5 a) 23 mm
b) 19.5 mm

Q6 a) £2230
b) All but one of the cars cost much less than this, while one costs a huge amount more.

Q7 E.g. The mean and median for the comedy films are lower than for the action films, so the comedy films tend to be shorter.
The range of the comedy films is shorter than the range of the action films, so the comedy films are more similar in length to each other, while the action films are more varied in length.

Q8 a) 249
b) 152
c) 97

Pages 110-112 — Simple Charts and Graphs

Q1 a) 24
b)

Milk	◈ ◇

c) 81

Q2 a) Monday, Wednesday and Thursday
b) Monday

Q3 a) 60%
b) 10% (accept ± 2%)

Q4

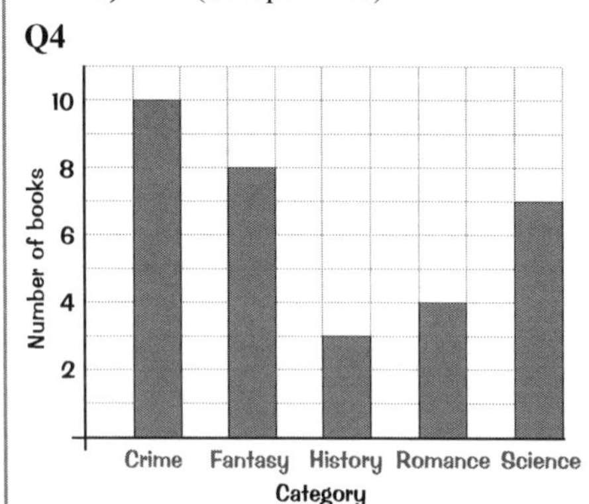

Q5 a) $6 + 17 = 23$
b) $79 + 53 + 31 + 9 = 172$
c) $6 + 17 + 29 + 79 + 53 + 31 + 9 = 224$
d) $\frac{79}{224}$

Q6

	Van	Motor-bike	Car	Total
Travelling North	15	12	21	48
Travelling South	20	9	23	52
Total	35	21	44	100

a) 35
b) 52
c) 9
d) 21

Q7 a) 3
b) 4
c) $(2 \times 1) + (4 \times 2) + (5 \times 3) + (4 \times 4) + (1 \times 5) = 46$
d) $2 + 4 + 5 + 4 + 1 = 16$ students were asked altogether, so the mean number of visits is $46 \div 16 = 2.875$
e) Median = 3
$P(3) = \frac{5}{16}$

Q8 a)

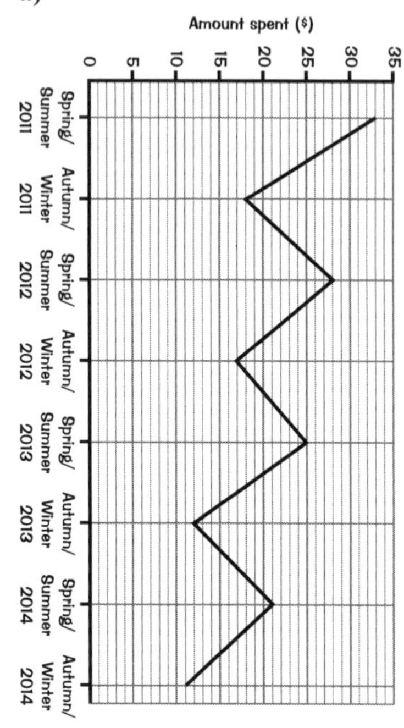

b) The amount spent on sun cream is steadily falling (although there is a rising and falling seasonal pattern).

Q9 a) The vertical axis is numbered so that the same size interval represents different amounts. This means that the test scores are falling much more quickly than the graph suggests.
b) The numbering on the vertical axis doesn't start at 0. This means the increase in scores is happening much less quickly than it appears from the graph.

Answers: P113 — P116

Page 113 — Pie Charts

Q1 **a)** $\frac{1}{3}$

b) £18 000

c) $\frac{1}{6}$

d) £9000

Q2

Activity	Hours	Working	Angle
Homework	6	6 ÷ 48 × 360° =	45°
Sport	2	2÷48×360°=	15°
TV	10	10÷48×360°=	75°
Computer games	2	2÷48×360°=	15°
Sleeping	18	18÷48×360°=	135°
Listening to music	2	2÷48×360°=	15°
Paid work	8	8÷48×360°=	60°
Total	48		360°

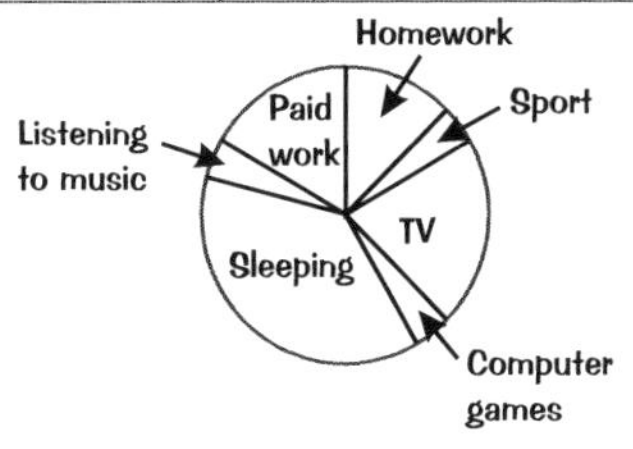

Q3 It's not possible to tell whether more people voted for the Green Party in 2010, because you can't tell how many people voted in either election.

Page 114 — Scatter Graphs

Q1 **a) i)** Moderate positive correlation

ii) The higher the temperature, the more ice cream sold.

b) i) Strong negative correlation

ii) The higher the price, the less ice cream sold.

c) i) No correlation

ii) There's no connection between the age of customers and the amount of ice cream they buy.

Q2 **a)** and **b)**

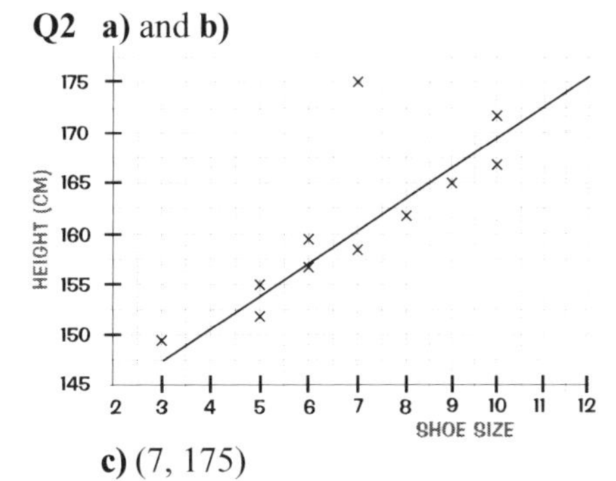

c) (7, 175)

d) There is positive correlation. The taller the pupil, the bigger their shoe size.

e) Size 4 (accept 3.5 to 4.5)

f) This is outside the range of the data.

Page 115 — Frequency Tables — Finding Averages

Q1 **a)** 5 hours

b)

Number of Hours	0	1	2	3	4	5	6	7	8
Frequency	1	9	10	10	11	27	9	15	8
Hours × Frequency	0	9	20	30	44	135	54	105	64

c) 461 hours

d) 461 ÷ 100 = 4.61 hours

Q2 **a)** 1

b) 1

c) 5

d) i)

GOALS	FREQUENCY	GOALS × FREQUENCY
0	7	0
1	11	11
2	6	12
3	4	12
4	3	12
5	1	5

ii) 52

iii) 52 ÷ 32 = 1.625 goals per game

Page 116 — Grouped Frequency Tables

Q1 **a)**

No. of Miles (thousands)	81 - 90	91 - 100
No. of Cars	3	1

b) 31 - 40 thousand miles

c) 41 - 50 thousand miles

d) 70 people drove more than 30 000 miles last year.
This is 70 ÷ 80 × 100 = 87.5% of the people.
Either: This is less than 90%, so the data does not support Dean's claim.
Or: This rounds to 90%, so the data does support Dean's claim.

Q2 **a)**

Time (t)	Frequency	Mid-interval value	Frequency × mid-interval
$30 \le t < 40$	4	35	140
$40 \le t < 50$	7	45	315
$50 \le t < 60$	8	55	440
$60 \le t < 70$	4	65	260

b) Total frequency = 23
Total of 4th column = 1155
So estimated mean
= 1155 ÷ 23
= 50.2 minutes (to 1 d.p.)

c) 40 minutes

Q3 **a)**

Dolphins			
Time interval (seconds)	Frequency (f)	Mid-interval value	f × mid-int'l
$14 \le t < 20$	3	17	51
$20 \le t < 26$	7	23	161
$26 \le t < 32$	15	29	435
$32 \le t < 38$	32	35	1120
$38 \le t < 44$	45	41	1845
$44 \le t < 50$	30	47	1410
$50 \le t < 56$	5	53	265

Sharks			
Time interval (seconds)	Frequency	Mid-interval value	f × mid-int'l
$14 \le t < 20$	6	17	102
$20 \le t < 26$	15	23	345
$26 \le t < 32$	33	29	957
$32 \le t < 38$	59	35	2065
$38 \le t < 44$	20	41	820
$44 \le t < 50$	8	47	376
$50 \le t < 56$	2	53	106

b) Dolphins
Mid interval × frequency column adds up to 5287.
Frequency column adds up to 137.
So estimated mean time
= 5287 ÷ 137 = 38.6 s (1 d.p.)

Sharks
Mid interval × frequency column adds up to 4771.
Frequency column adds up to 143.
So estimated mean time
= 4771 ÷ 143 = 33.4 s (1 d.p.)

CGP

MCFA46 £2.00 (Retail Price)

www.cgpbooks.co.uk